*Bay of the North*

# Bay of the North
### The Story of Pierre Radisson

## BY RONALD SYME

*Illustrations by Ralph Ray*

1950
WILLIAM MORROW AND COMPANY · NEW YORK

# CONTENTS

# Bay of the North

## Chapter One

*A FIGHT
IN THE FOREST*

Young Pierre Radisson stared out of a loophole in the high wooden stockade. Spring had come to Canada. The forest encircling the little French settlement of Three Rivers had turned a soft, lovely green. Pierre longed to walk across the fields and go in among the trees where he would find the trails of wild animals. He wanted to roam along those trails, stepping lightly on the deep, springy layer of pine needles underfoot.

9

But there were other things in the forest besides wolves and deer. The year was 1652. Every
spring, war parties of fierce Iroquois Indians
came up from the south. Their tomahawks were
freshly sharpened, their lean faces and shaven
heads smeared with war paint. During the summer months they roamed along the shores of the
St. Lawrence River, attacking the tiny French
settlements that lay in their path.

Pierre had arrived in Canada only a year ago,
but already he knew terrible things about these
Iroquois. Even before he had left the little fishing village of Saint-Malo on the coast of France,
he had heard dreadful stories that travelers
brought back across the Atlantic.

Pierre Radisson knew that even now war
parties might be prowling through the woods.
Fear of them kept the settlers behind their high
stockade. When the men went out to tend their
fields or graze their cattle, they were careful to
walk in small parties. Each man carried a musket
and a couple of pistols.

That sweet-smelling forest would be a wonderful place after a freezing winter behind high
wooden walls. But Pierre's parents had forbid-

den him to go outside the stockade. And Pierre knew they were right. The Iroquois would scalp any rash settler who went too far alone. A boy of sixteen would have no chance against them at all.

"Ho there, Pierre!"

Pierre looked round. Two young men were coming towards him. They were the sons of other settlers. Both of them were husky fellows of eighteen or nineteen. They were wearing fringed deerskin coats and stout leather knee breeches. From the broad straps across their shoulders hung pouches holding coarse black gunpowder and lead shot. Under their arms they were carrying long-barreled muskets.

"We're going into the forest," said one of the boys. "All winter we've eaten nothing but salted pork. Fresh meat will taste good after so long. Jean here saw a deer in the fields this morning."

"Come with us, Pierre," said the other lad. "The more guns the better."

Pierre looked at the hunters. Then he looked at the forest. He knew the danger and so did his friends. They wanted to be reckless and to boast of their courage afterwards. What a fine thing it would be to return later in the day carrying fat game and describing how far they had traveled in Indian country!

One of the young men noticed Pierre's hesitation.

"If you fear for your scalp," he taunted, "then stay here with your mother and sisters. We'll go alone."

Pierre's brown face grew angry. He was a strong young fellow, quick on his feet and afraid of nothing.

"I'm not afraid," he said. "Wait here for me."

A few minutes later the three hunters passed through the heavy door of the stockade, Pierre now carrying his own musket. A couple of pistols, loaded with heavy shot, were stuck in the wide leather belt round his waist. He had picked up his weapons without meeting any of his family. No one but himself and his friends knew anything of the hunting trip.

They crossed the sunny fields, joking and laughing, jumping over fallen tree trunks, glad to be away from the dreary little settlement. Soon they reached the edge of the dim, silent forest. Its gloom damped the high spirits of the hunters. They halted among the first trees and looked at one another with questioning eyes.

"Why do we hesitate?" asked one of Pierre's friends. "Let us swear here and now that we will all stand together, no matter what happens."

They shook hands. Then they chose different paths and prepared to start hunting. Pierre and one of the others began walking along the bank of the great river. The third youth entered the wood.

A mile farther on they all met in a clearing. They had seen nothing; not one of them had even fired a shot. It would be dangerous to go any farther from the settlement, but at last they decided to walk one more mile up the river. None of them liked the idea, but no one wanted to risk being called a coward for saying so.

Soon their luck changed. They came to a shallow, sunlit lake where there were hundreds of wild ducks. The three muskets began banging. Small white clouds of smoke drifted through the rushes. Birds came splashing down into the sparkling water.

"Let's go home now," said one of Pierre's companions. He waded ashore and dropped a fine plump duck on the ground. "We have enough

birds for everybody." He looked at the dark forest around them. "It would be stupid to go any
farther," he added.

Pierre suddenly realized how much he had
been enjoying himself. The good fresh air, the
sunshine, and the blue sky all seemed better outside that hateful stockade. This was the first
time he had walked through the forest. He did
not want to leave its green-and-brown beauty for
a long time yet.

"Go if you wish," he said. "I'll walk on alone."

"You're a fool to risk it," said the boy who
wanted to go home. "If there are any war parties
anywhere near here, they will have heard our
shots. The quicker we leave the better."

"I, too, wish to return," said the second young
man. "Be wise and come with us, Pierre."

Pierre shook his head. "I am going on," he
repeated firmly. "It isn't noon yet and I want to
shoot more birds."

They stood arguing for several minutes. The
others would not go any farther; in fact, they
were beginning to wish they had not come quite
so far. Pierre was determined to spend the afternoon hunting. At last it was settled. The other

two began walking back to Three Rivers. Pierre, feeling proud of himself, marched upriver through the forest.

Before long he came across as much game as any hunter could wish to see. He was loading and firing as fast as he could. Finally he had to stop and leave some of the birds he had shot in a hollow tree. He meant to pick them up when he came back that way later on. Meanwhile he walked on up the bank, enjoying every minute of his adventure.

The sun showed that it was late afternoon when Pierre got back to the hollow tree. He loaded two geese, a wild turkey, and twelve ducks on his shoulders. He was tired already and his load seemed to grow heavier with every step he took. When he had nearly reached the clearing where he had left his friends, Pierre dropped the birds and sat down beside them to rest. He wished that he had not come quite so far. He would have to walk fast to reach Three Rivers before sunset.

In the green twilight of the forest in front of him a stick snapped loudly, as if a foot had trodden on it.

The noise startled Pierre. He grabbed his musket and sat staring around him. The forest was dead quiet. Nothing, not even a bird, could be heard moving. Softly he drew out his pistols and made sure they were ready to fire. The powder in one of them seemed to have become wet. He cocked the hammer and pulled the trigger. There was a loud bang that must have been heard a mile away if anyone was listening. Pierre quickly reloaded, glancing up every now and then to make sure no Indians were creeping towards him. When the pistol was ready, he picked up his load, slung the musket on his shoulder, and started along the trail back to the settlement. His knees were trembling slightly—and not only because he was tired. Pierre was just a little scared.

Half a mile farther on, the path curved round to the left. He tramped along it, wondering if he would get a welcome or a scolding from his parents. Suddenly he gasped with fright and stopped dead. In the long grass beside the path two naked bodies lay sprawled, their white skins smeared with blood. In spite of his horror Pierre stepped a little closer and recognized his companions.

They were dead. One had been tomahawked, the other shot and stabbed. Both of them had been scalped.

His fright and shock started Pierre's nose bleeding. He stood staring a minute, then began to tiptoe towards the river bank with a handkerchief clutched to his nose. Before he reached the water, his eyes met another terrifying sight—a row of heads above the bushes! The faces were painted; tufted black locks of hair stood up on brown, shaven skulls. They were Iroquois! They had seen him!

Instead of dropping everything he was carrying and running for his life, Pierre, moved by a desperate courage, stopped and loaded his musket with a heavy lead ball. Carrying the weapon in one hand, he went on down the path that led to the river, shaking with fright. Could it be possible that the Iroquois had not noticed him? If they had, why were they taking so long to attack him?

In the forest close beside him a couple of muskets went off with loud bangs. Two bullets screamed over his head, their noise drowned by piercing Iroquois war cries. Indians came running and jumping at Pierre from among the trees.

Pierre dropped his birds. He raised the heavy musket to his shoulder, glanced along its barrel, sighted a charging figure, and squeezed the trigger. There was a roar and a red flash. The figure disappeared. Dropping the empty gun, Pierre grabbed his pistols. The screaming, running Indians were nearly on him now. He could see the gleam of their knives and axes. He sighted quickly and fired. The pistol banged and jumped in his hand. An Indian clutched his face and tumbled forward with a shriek. Pierre sighted carefully for his last shot and again pressed the trigger. Another Indian threw up his arms and went down. Pierre did not see him fall. Muscular arms had wrapped themselves round him and hurled him to the ground. Hard bony bodies fell on top of him, bruising him and nearly knocking him unconscious.

Pierre hoped desperately that the Iroquois would be angry enough to kill him then and there. He hoped to die like his friends. If his life was spared now, he knew what would happen to him later on. He would be dragged back to an Indian village and tortured to death in front of a laughing, yelling crowd of men, women, and children. Death from a tomahawk blow would be quicker and easier than dying at a stake in the midst of jeers. ✒

But Pierre did not die in that forest. Perhaps the Indians admired the white boy's courage in fighting back at them as they charged. Perhaps they were in a good temper because they had already killed two Frenchmen that day. They hauled Pierre to his feet, terrified him still further by waving his friends' scalps in front of his eyes, and then dragged him with them into the forest.

They made him walk five miles. Every time he stumbled, an Indian struck him across the shoulders with the handle of a tomahawk. Somehow he was able to keep going until the Iroquois reached their camp. By that time he was half-dead from weariness and fear.

The camp lay in a small patch of open ground near the river. Canoes were drawn up on the shore. Other Iroquois warriors were sitting or sprawling round a fire. The Indians began preparing a meal for themselves. Some of them tore

off Pierre's clothes, laughing as they patted his
white skin. They tied a rope round his waist
when they sat down to eat and made signs to
Pierre to squat beside them on the ground. Then
they tried to feed him.

Pierre was much too frightened to want to
eat. In any case, even if he had been dying of
hunger, he would have shrunk from eating that
horrible meal. Dried corn had been thrown into
a cooking pot. After it went meat that was rotten
and full of maggots. While the filthy mess was
still uncooked, the Indians began helping themselves with their hands. In spite of Pierre's dis-
taste, they forced him to swallow mouthful after
mouthful, making angry signs at him when he
shook his head.

Stars were shining when the party lay down
to sleep on the ground. A warrior gave Pierre a
thin cotton blanket and signed to him to wrap
himself up in it. When he stretched himself on
the earth, two warriors, one on each side, lay
down with him. Each of them had one end of the
rope round Pierre's waist. They were making
sure he did not try to escape.

Tired out, terrified, and feeling sick from the

dreadful food he had been obliged to eat, Pierre wondered miserably whether he would lie awake all night. Much to his surprise, he did not. He went to sleep almost as quickly as the Indians. When he woke up, the trees were visible against a gray morning sky.

For breakfast the Iroquois picked up last night's cooking pots and once more heated the food in them over the fire. Again they made Pierre eat with them. This morning, however, they no longer shouted and pretended to strike him. They went out of their way to find the least rotten parts of the meat and invited him to swallow them. Pierre did his best. He closed his eyes and gulped down the pieces, hoping that would please his captors.

As soon as the sun came up, the Iroquois packed their belongings into the canoes and made Pierre lie face down in the bottom of one. The party pushed off from the shore, singing, shouting, and laughing as they paddled upstream with long, easy strokes that sent the canoes shooting along with marvelous speed.

Pierre lay in his canoe for most of the day. He felt sick, he was as frightened as ever, and he

spent most of his time wondering what the
Iroquois were going to do with him. He still
hoped that they might grow tired of having him
with them and knock him on the head with an
ax, but somehow his wish for death was not quite
so strong this morning.

The splash of paddles and the singing stopped
when the sun was going down in the west. Pierre
carefully raised his stiff and aching body so that
he could stare over the side of the canoe. Ahead
of him he saw a mass of dark-green islands,
covered with trees. Around them flowed the
great St. Lawrence, its surface golden in the last
light of the sun. Pierre did not know it, but these
were the Isles of Richelieu. The Iroquois war
party from the south had chosen the islands for
their central camp.

Over two hundred warriors were already
there. Tepees were scattered on every island.
Cooking fires flamed and smoked beside them.
The fires were grilling good fresh meat, for there
was plenty of game along that stretch of river.
Pierre discovered that when he was given a fine
lump of freshly killed venison. He felt better
when he lay down to sleep that night, even

though the rope round his waist reminded him that he was still a prisoner.

The band of Indians who had captured Pierre spent three days idling round their fires. Every now and then one or two of them went off to hunt in the woods. No hunter ever came back without bringing a deer with him. Sometimes the Indians speared fish in the shallow water off the shore. They fed Pierre with everything they cooked, and as the days passed they began to treat him with much more kindness. Soon they gave him back his clothes.

One day some of the Iroquois decided to dress Pierre's hair in better style. He wore it long and his locks had become badly tangled and dirty since he had been taken prisoner. They combed it out with a rough comb carved out of wood. Then they dragged it backwards and tied it in a knot on top of his head. They ornamented the knot by winding a piece of red ribbon in and out of it. The warriors laughed when they admired the result. *"Chagon!"* they said to the solemn Pierre. *"Chagon!"*

Pierre had no idea what the word meant. He spent a good deal of time wondering about it.

Certainly he would have felt much better if he had known that it meant *cheer up*. The Iroquois were telling him not to be afraid.

When the party had been on the island a week, Pierre's guardian took the rope off his waist. He made signs that Pierre could now go wherever he pleased. It was impossible to go very far on a small island, but Pierre felt much more cheerful from then on. He was sorry when the time came to get back into the canoes.

This time he did not have to lie on his face. The Indian to whom Pierre seemed to belong gave him a paddle. Pierre sweated away with it, trying to show the Iroquois that he was doing his best and hoping to please everyone. He was not very skillful. The amount of water he threw all around and the number of times he nearly upset the canoe made everyone else shriek with laughter.

At last the Indian with Pierre stopped laughing and began giving him lessons in paddling. He showed Pierre how to make the smooth easy movements that would not tire him out even after a whole day's paddling. When the canoes were carried ashore that night, Pierre felt happier than he had since the Indians captured him, though he still had no idea what was going to happen to him in the end. Sometimes he dared to hope the kind treatment he was receiving meant that no one was going to hurt him. At other times he remembered the stories he had heard about the Iroquois. The torture stake haunted his dreams nearly every night.

The war party left the St. Lawrence and began traveling south up the Richelieu River. They were returning to their villages. Every day the fleet of canoes grew smaller. Warriors reached their homes, shouted farewell to their companions, and paddled ashore. The men with Pierre kept on. Their canoes entered Lake Champlain, skimmed southward along it, down another stream, and into the Mohawk River on whose shores stood their villages. Soon they would be home.

One night after they had eaten supper, the braves sharpened a knife and shaved Pierre's head, leaving only a long thick tuft of hair on top of it. This lock they stiffened with river clay and some of their own red paint. The work took several hours, but Pierre patiently waited until the Indians had finished. He thought that the more fun they had with him, the less willing they would be to torture him.

At last the Indians sat back on their heels and studied the results of their fun. One of them handed Pierre a small mirror in which he could admire his new appearance. But Pierre was not much amused. He had no wish to look like an Iroquois brave.

The Indians seemed to be growing fond of Pierre as the days went past. He was a cheerful lad and his good spirits began to return, in spite of his worry about what was going to happen to him. Sometimes he sang little French songs to the war party as they sat round the campfire. Pierre had a good voice and a fine sense of humor. Both gifts helped him to get along with Indians wherever he went. The Iroquois began teaching him words of their own language. Pierre was quick to learn them. At the end of a fortnight, he could understand a good deal of what was said to him and could make himself understood.

The Indian in Pierre's canoe told him that from now on they were brothers. The news

made Pierre still more cheerful. Surely, even
Iroquois would not torture their own brothers.
One morning Pierre's brother found him standing on the beach flourishing a sword. Like most
boys of his age in those days, Pierre could handle
a sword as well as firearms. The Indian grinned
approvingly. Later he took the sword and
showed Pierre one or two Iroquois tricks with it.

There was another reason why Pierre was so
popular with his captors. He could shoot much
better than any of them. The braves had quite
a few muskets in their canoes, but they did not
understand how to aim them. Often the war
party came across deer grazing along the banks.
It was always Pierre who picked up a musket and
shot the animal. The surrounding forests were
full of bears. When the Iroquois went hunting
them, they took Pierre and his gun. Bears were
the favorite food with the Indians and they
shouted with approval every time the boy shot
one. Pierre himself must have been just as glad.
He had no wish to return to a diet of that awful
meat he had been given on his first night as a
prisoner.

The Iroquois were getting near their own

settlements. They no longer camped in the forest at night, but stayed in one of the many villages dotted along the banks of the river. Pierre hated these villages. The Indians in them looked upon him merely as another white prisoner. Some teased him with wicked cleverness. A few struck him. All of them made it quite clear that white men were only good for the fiery stake.

Pierre did nothing to protect himself against these tormentors. He tried desperately to hide the fact that he was terribly frightened. Whenever an Indian hit him, he smiled and tried to make friends with the man. Something different happened one evening. He was given a chance to have a little revenge.

The war party had stopped for the night. A group of Indian boys of about Pierre's own age gathered to stare at him. They made loud remarks about his white skin and his stupidity in being taken prisoner. They shouted that he must be a coward. At last one of them stepped forward and smacked Pierre across the face.

Pierre could do nothing. He smiled at the boy and kept his hands down. To hit back might have meant all kinds of punishment. But his In-

dian brother had seen the blow and came running. He put his hand on Pierre's shoulder and
thrust him at the grinning youth.

"Do not be afraid," said the Iroquois. "We
will not harm you. Go, fight back at him who
struck you."

Those were the best words Pierre could have
heard. He was tired of being beaten and of being
unable to do anything about it. Now he was
actually being told to defend himself against the
Indian youth who stood in front of him, smirk-
ing.

Pierre leaped at the startled Indian, grabbed
his topknot, and punched him hard on the nose.
The Indian yelled and grabbed Pierre's own topknot. Pierre replied by clawing the Indian's face.
Then he unloosed another punch and followed
it up by biting the Indian's arm as hard as he
could.

This was going to be a good fight. The Iroquois came running from all over the village to
enjoy it. They formed a circle round the two
boys, yelling and shouting advice to both of
them.

The young Iroquois had been brought up in

the belief that white boys could not fight. Now
he was discovering the error of that belief. He
was going to have to fight as hard as he could if
he was to avoid being thrashed in front of his
own tribe. Pierre was equally determined to
defeat him. He knew that winning this fight
would make his own party of Indians even more
friendly towards him. He had to have as many
friends as he could.

The fight was dirty from start to finish. The
Indian tried to jab his fingers in Pierre's eyes.
Pierre bit the fingers until their owner roared
with pain. The Indian again grabbed Pierre's
topknot and tried to dash him to the ground.
Pierre slashed the Indian's face with his fingernails. They went into a clinch, each straining to
throw the other backward. The Indian soon felt
that Pierre's arms were stronger than his own.
He wriggled out of the clinch, stepped back a
pace, and tried to kick Pierre in the stomach.
That was a bad mistake. The Indian had bare
feet. Pierre was wearing good heavy shoes with
thick, nail-studded soles. The kick he landed on
the Iroquois made him bellow with pain.

Once again the Iroquois tried to grab Pierre's

topknot. Pierre seized the reaching hand, turned his back on his enemy, dragged the youth's arm over his shoulder, and levered the arm downward. It was a famous old wrestling trick that Pierre had learned from the French fishermen in Saint-Malo and it worked like a miracle. The Iroquois shot up in the air. He flew over Pierre's crouching shoulders, came down with a heavy thud, and lay sprawling on his back, gasping for breath and dizzy from the violence of his fall.

Pierre jumped on his chest, squatted there, and started pounding the Indian's face with his fists. At this point the cheering Iroquois came forward and dragged Pierre away from his bruised and bloody victim. That was the end of the fight.

Winning the battle was the best thing Pierre could have done. His brother clapped him on the back, washed the blood off his face, and gave him a fine supper that night. The other Iroquois braves grinned and joked with Pierre as he ate. Only one thing they said made Pierre start worrying all over again.

"Tomorrow," the Iroquois said smilingly, "we will reach our own village."

## Chapter Two

*PIERRE RADISSON
TRIES TO ESCAPE*

**P**IERRE lay down to sleep, wondering whether he would still be alive the next day. He felt almost as frightened as he had been when the Iroquois first attacked him. He slept badly and was staring wide-eyed over his blanket when the darkness paled into morning.

The Iroquois left their canoes on the shore. They walked into the forest and began following a twisting trail to their village. The trees thinned out after an hour's walking. Ahead of him Pierre saw bright green fields of corn. Beyond them was an untidy line of grayish-brown tents and huts, surrounded by a stockade of pointed wooden posts.

As the party emerged from the dim forest into bright sunshine, they were sighted by the villagers. A crowd began running towards them, shouting with joy and screeching cries of welcome. Pierre was quickly surrounded by a jabbering, smelly crowd of Indians. His war party kept him in their midst until they were a hundred yards from the big wooden gate leading into the village. There they halted.

"Take off your clothes," ordered Pierre's Indian brother.

Shocked and surprised, Pierre began to do as he was told. He guessed what was going to happen. The excited Indians had placed themselves in two lines facing inward. Their cruel faces were eagerly turned towards him. In their hands they were holding sticks, iron bars, heavy leather whips, knives, and wooden clubs. They were already waving these weapons with fierce glee. Pierre knew he was expected to run between those two lines. Every one of the Indians in the lines would strike him with whatever he held in his hand. There would be little chance of his ever reaching the wooden gate in the stockade.

This was the end, thought Pierre, as he unfastened his shirt with shaking fingers. He had been a fool to think that the Iroquois had meant anything by the kindness they had shown him during the trip. They had no intention of sparing him torture. Even his brother was helping him to strip. There was a tiny chance that if he ran fast enough he might pass through the lines and reach the village. But was it worth while trying to escape one kind of torture merely to suffer many others? Pierre was still wondering about that when he was hauled, naked, to the starting point.

At that moment an old woman suddenly stepped out of the crowd and threw a blanket round his bare shoulders. She caught him by the hand, then turned and said a few words to the Iroquois braves. When she had finished speaking, she drew Pierre after her to a small hut.

"Sit down," she said, and silently began preparing a meal over a small fire.

Pierre sat staring round him, wondering what was going to happen next. At every second he expected to be dragged out of the hut by the braves who came to peer in at him from the entrance. This treatment was certainly something he had never expected. He wondered when it would end.

Pierre did not know that the Iroquois women, especially the older women, were treated as very important people by the warriors. They had the right to save from torture any prisoner to whom they took a fancy. This kindly old squaw had heard about Pierre's bravery when he was attacked in the forest. Someone had also told her about Pierre's skill with a gun and the way he had won the fight with the Iroquois boy. When she threw a blanket across his shoulders, she showed that she was willing to adopt him into her family. From now on Pierre would be treated by the tribe as her son.

Pierre began to realize how lucky he had been as the day went on. One of the old woman's daughters combed his hair, gave him water to wash his face, and handed him the daintiest bits of meat from a fine hot plate of stew. At first Pierre was too frightened to eat. Slowly his courage came back and he tried to thank the old woman in the few native words he knew.

The following day he made another discovery. The squaw was the wife of the tribe's chief. In other words, his adopted father was the most powerful man in the village.

Pierre really enjoyed himself during the next two months. There were three daughters in the family and they soon grew fond of their white brother. When the old chief gave Pierre a gun, the young Indian girls went with him into the fields and watched him shoot small animals or birds for food. They took him to other tents in the village, taught him to speak their language, made new clothes for him of fine deerskin, and cooked him delicious meals. By the time summer arrived, Pierre could talk the Iroquois tongue nearly as well as the Indians themselves. He was friendly with almost everyone in the village and took part as a guest in all the feasts and games. He had a gift for making people like him.

"Tell me, of what race are you?" his foster mother asked him one day. She spoke in Huron, the language of a northern tribe who lived near Three Rivers and were friendly with the French.

"I am a *Penugaga* (Iroquois)," Pierre replied quickly. He spoke Huron well enough to under-

stand the question but he carefully replied in
Iroquois.

The old woman was delighted. "From now on
your name will be Orimha," she said. "Once I
had a son of that name. He was killed in battle.
I was a Huron, but the Iroquois raided my village when I was a child and brought me back
here with them. Now I am an Iroquois. And you,
you are Orimha, my son."

There the story of Pierre Radisson might have
ended, and if it had, Canada would have lost one
of her most famous explorers. Other white cap-
tives had been lucky enough to be adopted by
Indian tribes. Most of them settled down to
their new lives, grateful not to have been killed.
Only a few of them ever thought of escaping and
still fewer tried it. But Pierre hated the idea of
remaining too long in any one place. He was
like that all his life.

One day three young Indian braves asked him
to go hunting with them. Pierre's mother gave
him permission. The four young men set out
for the woods, Pierre's sisters carrying his heavy
pack and his musket until they reached the forest. There the girls said good-by to him and the

other hunters and turned back to the village.

The first day's hunting was bad. When evening came they had killed nothing. Early next morning they started off again, walking slowly along the bank of the Mohawk River. They stopped later in the day and Pierre watched his three companions cut the bark off a birch tree, curve it into shape, lace the open ends with deer hide and, in three hours, make a canoe big enough for all four of them.

They paddled downstream, trying to reach a spot where there was more game. Before long they came to a place where another little river flowed into the Mohawk. A small lake had formed here and its surface was covered with ducks. On the shores grew thick bushes and trees. In this cover lurked plenty of fine fat deer, some of which the four hunters killed with their guns. That night and the next Pierre and his companions grilled juicy fat steaks of venison over the glowing logs on their fire.

They were on their way back to the village when they met another Indian. He, too, had been hunting and asked if he might join the party.

Pierre was wearing moccasins and a strip of cloth round his middle. His white skin had been darkened by the summer sun until it was as dark as an Indian's. His sisters had gone on dressing his topknot and shaving the rest of his head. He spoke Iroquois but he was still not an Indian. The stranger stared at him for a while.

When they were alone he spoke. "You are an *Asseroni* (Frenchman)," he said to Pierre in the Indian tongue. "My heart would be glad to see Three Rivers again."

"And also mine," said Pierre without thinking. He stopped quickly when he realized what he had said.

"Do not be afraid," said the other man. "I am a Huron. Some years ago the Iroquois took me prisoner but spared my life and took me into their tribe. Is your heart yet with your own people?"

"Is your heart yet with your own tribe?" asked Pierre.

It was a clever answer. The Indian smiled. Quickly he stepped closer to Pierre.

"Let us escape together," he whispered. "I know the way from here to Three Rivers. Tonight, while the others are asleep, we will kill them."

Pierre hated the idea of killing them, asleep or awake. The young Iroquois braves trusted him. He had been adopted into their tribe.

"No," he said. "I could not do such a thing."

The Huron sneered. "The Iroquois have killed and tortured many French people," he said. "Do you love a tribe who have burned the homes of your race and murdered even little children? Shall I escape alone and tell your friends in Three Rivers that you did not want to come back to them?"

Pierre began to feel tempted.

The Huron went on talking fiercely. "Do you not want to see your father and mother again?" he asked. "Do you not think that they want to see you?"

The Indian was right. Pierre was suddenly filled with longing to be with his family again. He knew there was no way of escaping while the Iroquois braves remained alive. They would come after him when they found him gone. Yes, they would have to be killed.

Tears came into Pierre's eyes as he nodded his

head. "Very well," he said sadly. "I will do as you say."

They remained awake that night after their companions had rolled into their blankets and gone to sleep. The Huron sat up quietly and reached out for a tomahawk on the ground. He handed it to Pierre.

"Strike when you see me strike," he whispered. "See! Here is an ax that will serve me well."

Pierre, hating what he had to do, crept over to the nearest sleeper. The Indian chose another victim. They struck at the same time. Two of the Iroquois died instantly. The Huron tomahawked the third, and Pierre, to make sure the man was dead, picked up his musket and shot him through the heart.

They stood listening until the tremendous echoes of the shot had died away in the silent forest. The Huron suddenly stooped and scalped the three Iroquois. Next he dragged the bodies to the river and hurled them into the water. Now the way to escape was prepared.

They loaded the canoe in a few minutes, pushed out into the darkness of the river, and began paddling as fast as they could. Hour after hour they fled down the Mohawk, at last reaching the Hudson River where they turned north. They stopped only when the sky began to grow light. Sweating and tired out, they landed on rocks where they would leave no footprints. They rushed the canoe into the forest, hid themselves beside it, and prepared to wait until darkness returned. The river was too dangerous for them by daylight.

A steady drizzle soaked them to the skin. Mosquitoes whined through the damp warm air and bit incessantly. Smoke would drive them away, but the smoke of a fire might be seen by watchful enemies.

As soon as it became dark, Pierre and the Huron carried the canoe back to the river. Once again they paddled all night. Day after day went by. Sometimes they hid in swamps, sometimes in dark, lonely forests. At other times they paddled the canoe into high clumps of reeds and slept in the little craft until sunset. No one saw them during the whole voyage. Seventeen days later they reached the St. Lawrence, and the Huron told Pierre that they were getting near Three

Rivers. By tomorrow evening he would be safely behind the French stockade.

It was dawn when Pierre heard this exciting news. The canoe was safely hidden. Pierre and the Huron had eaten their breakfast of dried meat and corn. They were lying rolled in their blankets and Pierre went off to sleep, thinking about the joy of seeing his family again.

Later the Huron awakened him. "Come, let us go," he said.

Pierre stared round him. It was only the middle of the afternoon. "We must wait until it is dark," he said. "To go along the river now is dangerous. There may be Iroquois war parties somewhere close by."

The Huron insisted on leaving at once. "If you do not come with me," he said, "I will go alone. I can wait no longer to see my own people."

Pierre had to go. He did not know this part of the river and it would be impossible for him to find his way to Three Rivers without a guide. Even so, he insisted that a daylight journey was not safe. They were still arguing about it when they launched the canoe. On that fine sunny afternoon they began the last few hours of their flight.

The St. Lawrence became very wide before they had gone more than a mile. Its surface was empty. Quickly they began paddling across it, trying to reach Three Rivers before darkness came.

The canoe was halfway across when Pierre thought he saw something far ahead of them. The heat was shimmering on the water and it was impossible to make out the object clearly. But Pierre thought that it was something moving along. He pointed it out hurriedly to his Indian companions.

"A flight of geese," said the Huron after staring for a few seconds. "There is nothing to fear from them."

They paddled on in silence. Pierre felt frightened but he could not have said why. He knew that danger was close. For the next few minutes he continued staring over the canoe's bow at that strange cloud on the horizon. Suddenly he saw why the Huron had thought it was a flock of low-flying geese. Pierre could see something moving up and down now, like the beat of wings.

But they were not wings. They were Indian paddles!

"Iroquois!" screamed Pierre. "A war party in canoes!"

The Huron realized his dreadful mistake after one quick look. They turned the canoe as quickly as they could. The shore was a couple of miles away but it was possible that they might reach it without being sighted. Once they were in the forest it would be nearly impossible to catch them. They paddled as fast as their weary arms could move.

Pierre had seen the danger too late. Big canoes, each thrust forward by five or six Indians, came flying out ahead of the advancing fleet. They were coming straight for Pierre and his companion.

The shore was still a mile distant when the Huron knew that they could never get there in time. He reached into the bottom of the canoe and flung the three Iroquois scalps overboard. They floated on the water, their topknots showing which tribe the men had belonged to. Indians in the leading canoe bent over the side and snatched them out of the water. They howled with rage as they saw that the scalps were Iroquois. The pursuers drove their canoes on with every scrap of strength in their shoulders. No one who had taken Iroquois scalps was going to escape revenge.

Pierre's canoe was three hundred yards from the shore when the Indians began shooting. Bullets whined off the water or whistled overhead. A few struck the canoe. Water began spurting into it from little round holes in its sides. Then came more shots. The Huron, sitting in the bow, suddenly flung out his arms and fell backward. He had been hit by three bullets and was badly wounded.

There was nothing more Pierre could do. He was unable to protect himself, for their three muskets were already under water and their powder useless. The bigger canoes swept alongside. Iroquois arms reached out and seized Pierre in a rough grip. He was hauled out of his sinking craft and thrown into the bottom of the Iroquois canoe. Other Indians dragged the dying Huron aboard.

The entire fleet pressed on to the shore. Forty canoes were drawn up out of the water. This was a big party of Iroquois. Pierre guessed there must be a hundred and fifty of them. They were in full war paint and had been raiding the countryside round Three Rivers. With them were other prisoners, six unfortunate Frenchmen and twenty Hurons—men, women, and children. From the bow of every canoe dangled a line of scalps.

Pierre was rushed up the beach. His Huron companion was still alive but no longer worth torturing. An Iroquois chopped off his head with an ax and stuck it on a pointed stick planted in the ground. Other Iroquois braves ripped off Pierre's clothes and slammed him against a wooden post. They roped him savagely round his neck, waist, knees, and ankles. On either side of him, other prisoners were being treated in the same way.

The Indians then sat down to eat. Pierre was left tied to the post for the whole night. His naked body smarted and stung under the bites of swarms of mosquitoes. But Pierre was past caring about such a minor torment as insect bites. Before leaving him the Iroquois had brought out a pair of pincers. With vicious joy they had torn off one of his fingernails. The pain was frightful, yet Pierre knew it was nothing compared with what he would have to suffer before long. This time there would be no one to save him from what he had always dreaded—the torture stake.

## Chapter Three

## THE TORTURE STAKE

THREE weeks later Pierre Radisson stared miserably across familiar cornfields. He was back in the Iroquois village from which he had fled. His voyage down from the St. Lawrence and up the Mohawk River had been a nightmare. He was treated as cruelly as the rest of the prisoners. The Iroquois braves kicked and struck him and this time there was no Indian brother to protect him. He had gone hungry. He had been questioned for hours at a time while tied to a post. During these ordeals he had

53

often fainted away from pain and exhaustion.

Now the villagers were forming into their two lines. Along with the other prisoners, Pierre was dragged to the starting point. A scream of fury came from the Indians when they saw him. They had all heard about the three floating scalps and were wild to revenge their dead. Pierre knew he would have to run along that double line. And he knew that he would never be allowed to reach the village alive.

Someone called him. "Orimha! Orimha!" He heard the familiar name above the shouting of the Indians.

Pierre looked round. Tears ran down his cheeks as he saw his foster mother struggling towards him through the crowd. Her arms were stretched out in sorrowful greeting.

At last she reached his side. "Orimha!" she lamented. "Why did you leave me, my son? Were you not happy with us?"

The first prisoner was already stumbling between the lines. He was a Frenchman. His shoulders and head were bowed as he tried to protect himself from the cruel blows. In a few minutes Pierre would be doing the same.

His foster mother seized his hand. "Come!" she exclaimed.

She spoke quickly to the nearest men. They scowled at Pierre but did not try to stop him when his foster mother dragged him out of the line of doomed prisoners. Hastily she guided him to the family hut. His adopted father, the chief, was already there. For half an hour he scolded Pierre, telling him that he had done a wicked and foolish thing in trying to escape. Then his anger died down.

"*Chagon!*" said the old man. "Let us eat. Afterward we will talk again."

Pierre's punishment had been postponed. Terrified though he was by the cries of French prisoners undergoing torture outside, he never lost his wits. His only chance for life was to invent a story that might appease the angry Iroquois.

He and his three companions had met the Huron in the forest, he said. After speaking with them for a while, the stranger had gone away. Late that night he had crept back while they all lay asleep round the fire and had killed the three Iroquois.

"Come with me," he had said to Pierre. "If you stay here, the Iroquois in the village will think you killed these men yourself." Pierre had seen his danger and had fled with the Huron.

The old chief listened to this story made up of truth and lies. He seemed to believe most of it. When he had finished eating, he went off to speak with the elders of the tribe. These old men acted as judges of offenses such as Pierre's.

The elders listened to Pierre's story. Some shook their heads; others nodded. No one quite knew what to believe. But the boy would have to be punished, they said. Yes, he would have to be punished. Killed? They would talk about that later on.

A crowd of braves came racing to the hut. They seized Pierre and dragged him outside. Behind him the boy could hear the heartbroken wailing and sobbing of his Indian sisters and foster mother. He believed that his last hour had come. In the distance he could see a Frenchman tied to a blazing stake. Even as he stared, an Iroquois chopped off the man's head.

Pierre was tied to a fire-blackened wooden stake and the braves tore off four of his fingernails. He fainted. The braves went away and left him to recover. Shortly before sunset an Indian squaw arrived, leading a small boy by the hand. She gave him a knife when they stopped and told him to hack off one of Pierre's fingers. Either the knife was too blunt or the child had not enough strength to do the job. He grew tired and went away before he had done much damage.

Pierre spent the night tied to his post. Next morning the Iroquois gathered round him again. The other prisoners were dead or dying. There was no further sport to be had with them.

An old man smoking a pipe sat down beside Pierre. He took hold of the boy's thumb and brutally rammed it down on top of the glowing tobacco.

Pierre's foster mother was watching the lad's dreadful pain from a distance. She did not dare to interfere until the old man had gone away. Then she approached and dressed Pierre's charred fingers with ointment. Before she had finished, the braves returned. They lit flaming torches and hurled them at Pierre's bare feet and legs. They pulled out more of his fingernails and scorched the palms of his hands with flaming embers. One of the braves came up carrying a sword which he had heated in a fire until it was red-hot. He plunged the blade through Pierre's left foot, pinning it to the ground. Pierre fainted again.

The Iroquois dosed him with a bitter drink of some kind. Satisfied when they saw him open his eyes, they went away. Only one old man tried to continue the torture. He started to cut off Pierre's thumb with a hunting knife, but the old chief angrily told him to stop.

Pierre had taken his terrible punishment with great bravery. Even the Iroquois were surprised at his courage. Word of it reached the hut where his family were still begging the elders to save the boy's life. The chief pointed out that the tribe would gain by having so brave a youth in their village. His wife likewise implored the elders to save her son from death. Meanwhile, Pierre's sisters had timidly come to where he stood at the stake and had done their best to dress his many wounds and burns.

It was his courage that saved Pierre. At long last the old men agreed that it would be wrong

to put so courageous a youth to death. The tribe
had need of such warriors as he.

Rejoicing greatly, Pierre's foster mother came
hurrying through the village to release him from
the stake. The braves who had been torturing
him only a short while ago crowded round to
help. Such was Pierre's joy, that when his
wounds and burns had been bandaged, he staggered round in an Indian dance until midnight.
His foster mother took him then to the hut,
bathed his wounds again, and put him to bed.
A month passed before he was properly cured.
He made an amazing recovery. His only lasting
damage was a stiff finger on his left hand, probably the one that the small boy had tried to saw
off.

Autumn turned to winter. The Iroquois were
busy talking over plans for war parties in the
spring. Pierre, having been forgiven, was invited
to go with ten braves who intended to raid a hostile tribe living on the southern shore of Lake
Erie.

Spring had not yet come when the party set
out from the village. Patches of snow covered
the ground. The flooded streams were full of

melting ice and the trees were black and bare. Traveling at such a time was a cold business. The young men waded through freezing streams, plodded across snow-filled valleys, and merely laughed when their thin clothes froze to their skins.

At last they reached enemy country. They hid in the forest near by and began attacking small parties of Lake Erie Indians. They crept after their victims through the frozen bushes and struck them down without mercy. Fishermen were killed while they handled their nets. Women drawing water from the lake were killed like everyone else. Lonely hunters from the villages died suddenly before they had reached their traps. It was a cruel, bloodthirsty business. Pierre saw plenty of killing during that spring but he did little or none himself. He hated the cruelty of the Iroquois. He was content to do the yelling and whooping while the rest of his party did the killing. Yet the Iroquois were delighted with their white brother's clever ideas and careful scouting. Only one warrior was slain in a fight. The rest went back to the village, loaded with scalps and prizes. Even Pierre had

an Indian girl as his prisoner. He gave her as a
slave to his foster mother when they reached
home.

Pierre's war party praised him to the whole
tribe. They said he was fearless, cunning, and
able to run faster and march longer than any of
them. The Iroquois loaded him with presents,
invited him to all their feasts, and thoroughly
spoiled him. He had become one of the most
popular braves in the village in spite of his
youth.

Summer came. The Iroquois were restless
after their spring fighting. They made up their
minds to set out on another kind of journey.
The country to the south was dotted with Dutch
settlements which had gradually spread inland
from the coast. The Dutch were anxious to exchange knives, muskets, cloth, kettles, and other
goods for precious beaver skins. These pelts were
sent to Europe and sold for a great deal of money.

The Iroquois knew how the Dutch wanted
pelts. There were no beavers near the Mohawk
River, but the tribe soon found a way around
that difficulty; they merely raided tribes in Canada who had plenty of them. They brought the

skins south and traded them to their friends, the Dutch.

The spring fighting had captured two hundred pelts. The Iroquois thought they might as well exchange them now for more useful things. Pierre was in the big party of Indians that started south. They marched across what later became New York State, killing game for the cooking pots as they went. After five days they reached Fort Orange (now Albany) on the Hudson River. By this time Pierre had traveled over more of North America than any other European had even dreamed of. His strange journey from the St. Lawrence down to Fort Orange was wonderful training for his future travels across unknown country.

Fort Orange was only a muddy village surrounded by a high palisade, but to Pierre it must have seemed an enormous town. There was a main street with two-storied stone or wooden houses on either side. In the center was a large fort. There was even a row of shops with shelves bending under the weight of goods from Holland. Dutchmen and their families walked the streets in good sturdy clothes, and soldiers in bright uniforms hung about the entrance to the fort.

Into this peaceful village strolled Pierre Radisson with his mob of painted and feathered companions. They wandered along the street, laughing and singing, sometimes stopping to sell a beaver skin or buy a trinket.

A French soldier leaning against a wall looked at Pierre as he went past. Young warriors, smeared with red paint and carrying muskets or tomahawks, were not an unusual sight in Fort Orange. Yet the Frenchman took a second look at this finely built young savage. The look became a stare.

"Oh, man," he finally called in Iroquois, "art thou not a Frenchman?"

Pierre was fearful of angering his companions. He wanted them to forget his white skin. "You speak foolishly," he replied in Iroquois. "We are brothers, these warriors and I."

"No!" insisted the soldier. "You are certainly French."

So certain was he that Pierre was French, there was no use denying it any longer. "Yes, that is true," Pierre admitted.

The Frenchman yelled with delight. He
called everyone in the street to come and look
at his unusual fellow countryman. Pierre, with
his shaven head, his stiff topknot of hair, and his
reddened skin, found himself surrounded by a
curious but friendly crowd of Dutch.

Luckily the Iroquois were pleased by this
sudden interest in their brother. They led him
through the streets, shouting and dancing with
glee. They showed him off to every white man
they met. The governor of Fort Orange at last
came out himself to see what all the noise was
about. He listened with amazement to Pierre's
account of his adventures, starting with the
shooting trip into the woods beyond Three
Rivers. When Pierre finished, the goodhearted
governor offered to buy him back from the Indians then and there.

This was a good chance for Pierre to secure
the freedom he had so much wanted. He longed
to accept, but he was afraid. He had not forgotten the torture stake. The Iroquois might be
angry if he left them now and went back to the
white people. One day he might fall into their
hands again.

Pierre refused the governor's offer. He left the Dutchman staring after him in surprise and spent the rest of the afternoon drinking beer with the townspeople. When the Iroquois left Fort Orange, Pierre went with them. The French soldier walked as far as the gate, begging him to change his mind and stay behind.

The braves went back to their village carrying loads of Dutch goods. Pierre's foster mother and sisters made a great fuss over him, fed him enormous meals, and exclaimed joyfully over the good iron kettle, the knives, beads, mirrors, and other presents he had brought them.

Now, too, Pierre's adventures might have ended. He had turned down a chance to get away from the Iroquois. The villagers liked him, he lived comfortably, and his Indian family adored him. It would have been easy for him to marry a young Indian girl and settle down with the tribe for the rest of his life.

Pierre did nothing of the sort. A month after he returned from Fort Orange he became restless again. Perhaps he missed the good Dutch tobacco, the well-spiced meat pies, the strong beer, and all the other pleasant things he had en-

joyed there. Pierre appreciated good food and
drink. All his life he liked to try new dishes.

Finally Pierre made up his mind to run away
again. Not even the fear of torture could hold
him back. This time, however, he made careful
plans for his escape. While he had been with the
Iroquois, he had learned how to be cunning. He
was no longer the ignorant boy in heavy European clothes who had gone wandering alone
through the woods with a musket under his arm.
He was a half-naked young Iroquois, tough and
fierce. Armed with an ax or a knife, he could go
anywhere unafraid.

Pierre told his foster mother that he wanted to
go on a hunting trip. He spent several days
sharpening his ax, cleaning his gun, and getting
his sisters to mend his moccasins. He told everyone in the village the same story about going
hunting. The Iroquois wished him luck and
thought nothing more about it. Braves often
went off alone when they grew tired of the village. Certainly no one had any suspicions. The
Indians knew how he had refused to be bought
by the Dutch in Fort Orange. They never
thought he might want to go back there now.

At last everything was ready. Pierre got up one morning as soon as it was daylight. He picked up a light ax and stuck a knife in his belt. His gun, his deerskin coat, and all his other belongings he left lying in the hut. No brave would start off on a long journey clad only in moccasins and a breechclout, so the Indians would not be suspicious about his departure. He walked slowly to the point where the path through the forest began. Once he was hidden by the trees he began running with long, easy strides. He kept it up all day, carefully avoiding trails where he might meet people from his own tribe.

He swam rivers, scaled hillsides, ran across mile after mile of bare plain and through great patches of forest. The sun went down. Pierre still ran. The moon came up and by its shadowy light he could find his way. His long brown legs kept carrying him over wild, lonely country where no European had ever been before. Towards morning the moon set. Somehow he managed to keep moving. When day broke and a cold wind came moaning across the deserted countryside, he was stiff and tired. He stopped for half an hour, ate a little dried meat, and then went on. He ran all

the morning, ran all the afternoon, and sighted
Fort Orange two hours before sunset.

Pierre did not dare to go straight into the
town. He was afraid there might be other Iroquois in the place. Close to where he stopped was
the hut of a Dutch settler. The white man was
amazed to be asked by a dusty, sweating young
Indian for pen and paper with which to write
a letter to the governor.

The Dutchman fetched writing materials
from a cupboard. He stared in astonishment as
the Iroquois rapidly wrote a note in the French
language. Pierre handed him the letter and
begged him to take it as quickly as possible to the
town. The settler agreed to do so.

Pierre hid in the hut until night, when he
heard voices outside. The Dutchman had come
back, bringing three soldiers from the fort, one
of them the Frenchman who had spoken to
Pierre. They brought with them a suit of European clothes. After Pierre had dressed himself in
the strange garments, they all set off to Fort
Orange. An hour later he was safely inside the
town.

The Iroquois came looking for Pierre. They

reached the town about a week later. While the boy lay hidden by the friendly governor, he heard the sad voices of his foster mother and sisters calling, "Oh, Orimha, Orimha. Come back to us, Orimha!" Warriors searched many of the houses and roamed through the streets, asking the Dutch for news of their brother. They could get none. At last they left Fort Orange in despair.

Pierre had one last glimpse of his weeping foster mother and sisters being led away kindly by the young braves. He himself must have felt sad at that moment. His life with the Iroquois was over. Never again was he to live as a brave with a loving family to care for him.

A month later he was sailing across the Atlantic in a ship bound for Holland.

## Chapter Four

## DANGEROUS JOURNEY

Pɪᴇʀʀᴇ had no wish to return to
Europe. He went there only because it was the
quickest way of getting back to the St. Lawrence
River. Few ships went up to Canada from Fort
Orange, but many sailed to Quebec and Mon-
treal from France.

Pierre, unfortunately, reached Holland during the winter. It took him three months to reach
his home town of Saint-Malo and find a ship that
would carry him back across the Atlantic. By that

time he must have been wildly impatient. The wretched poverty of France, the crowded streets, and the dreary lives of the people seemed worse to him now that he had seen the bright forests and clean spaces of America.

At last a sturdy little fishing boat carried him westward and landed him on the shores of the St. Lawrence. The year was 1654.

His family were overjoyed when he walked into their house at Three Rivers. They had thought he was dead—killed by the Iroquois like his two young friends. They listened for hours on end while he told them his strange and wonderful story.

There is no record of Pierre's doings until 1657. In July of that year he started off on another kind of trip. An Indian tribe called the Onondaga lived south of Lake Ontario in the area between Lake Oneida and Niagara Falls. They were on friendly terms with the French, for a few years earlier soldiers from Quebec had built a fort near the lake and had lived in it ever since. The Onondaga wanted more white men to come and live among them, to whom they could sell plenty of beaver pelts.

The French agreed to send a party. Missionaries asked Pierre to go with it as guide. He already knew more than anyone else about Indian tribes and he spoke two of their languages, Huron and Iroquois.

Pierre agreed. He may have wished he had not when he saw who were among the members of his party—eighty Iroquois braves. Luckily none of them knew him. There were also a hundred Hurons—men, women, and children. The Hurons had been so badly hammered by the savage Iroquois that the survivors longed to find a new home where they might live in peace. The Iroquois voyagers had promised not to hurt the Hurons during the trip. Twenty Frenchmen, including Pierre and a priest, Father Ragueneau, completed the party.

Pierre must have known that the chance of peace among such a crowd was about the same as it would be in a room full of fat mice and hungry cats! However, he shrugged his shoulders, picked up his musket, and climbed into one of the canoes.

The party started up the St. Lawrence River. The very first night the Iroquois decided that

peace with the French was a waste of good fighting time. Forty of them sneaked away in their canoes, hastened down to Montreal, and scalped a few Frenchmen and Hurons.

A couple of days later a small party of Hurons deserted, having guessed there was going to be trouble. Before the canoes reached Lake Ontario, two Iroquois in Pierre's canoe tomahawked and shot a Huron who was traveling with them. They threw his body into the water and paddled ashore as if nothing had happened. Pierre was furious but he did not dare to interfere. He and the other Frenchmen also landed and began cooking the midday meal in the usual manner.

Suddenly there came a screaming Iroquois war cry. Forty warriors came leaping and running out of the forest and were joined by their tribesmen from the canoes.

There were only twenty or thirty Huron braves in the party, but they did their best to protect the women and children with them. They formed a ring round them as the Iroquois charged. There was a fierce stabbing, hacking fight. When it was over, only two Huron men were left alive. They were old and had taken no part in the battle.

Neither Pierre nor the other Frenchmen risked interfering. They picked up their muskets, formed a group, and prepared to fight if their turn came. But the blood-stained Iroquois told poor Father Ragueneau, the priest, that now they were satisfied. The Frenchmen and the Huron women and children could go wherever they liked.

Pierre grew more and more worried. He began quarreling with the Iroquois warrior who shared his canoe. Before long they were splashing one another with their paddles. After that there was only one thing to do. They landed and fought it out on the beach with fists and feet. The Indian was a huge young fellow but Pierre was in a huge temper. They pounded one another half-unconscious and then staggered back into the canoe. Every day or so, from then on, they climbed ashore and had another fight.

The fleet reached Lake Ontario and paddled westward, keeping close to the shore. Pierre, weary from paddling and fighting, fixed up a sail in his canoe and sat back while the wind carried

him along at a fine speed. Everything went well
until he tried steering across the mouth of a wide
bay instead of sticking close to shore. A sudden
squall swept over the water when they were half-
way across. The canoe was carried out into the
rough lake. Pierre and his quarrelsome companion spent the rest of the day and most of the
night furiously blaming each other for the mis-
hap and bailing as fast as they could in order to
keep afloat.

This would have been a peaceful and pleasant
trip if it had not been spoiled by the warlike Iroquois. Every kind of deer could be found in the
forests along the shore. The lake was filled with
big fighting fish which Pierre speared or caught
with a line. Lovely summer weather lasted from
the time the canoes left Three Rivers until they
reached the Onondaga fort. Yet all the Frenchmen, as well as the frightened Huron women,
were delighted when they reached the southern
end of Lake Ontario and saw the stout fort in
the distance.

Forty Frenchmen were in the garrison of the
fort. They had tilled the surrounding fields and
grown wonderful crops of vegetables and fruit.

Pigs squealed and grunted in shaded enclosures.
Fish swarmed in the lake. The forests were rich
in wild game of every kind. The place was a paradise after the misfortunes and dangers of the
four-hundred-mile trip which Pierre's fleet had
made.

But a week later trouble came to this paradise.
The Onondaga had not invited the Frenchmen
to their country merely because they liked having white faces round them. They believed that
every Frenchman was eager to trade goods for
beaver pelts. The Indians thought that if they
could exchange their skins right here at the fort,
it would save them the long and dangerous canoe
journey to Montreal or some other settlement.
They became bad-tempered when they discovered that Father Ragueneau was more interested
in saving souls than in buying beaver skins.

By autumn the Indians had begun to discuss
an attack on the fort. They became even more
pleased with the idea when four hundred more
Iroquois appeared. They were mostly from the
Mohawk River. Their leader was Pierre's tough
old foster father, the chieftain.

There was no immediate trouble from the

Iroquois. Pierre, surrounded by other well-
armed Frenchmen living in a fort, was a very different person from the scared boy who had wandered alone through the forest. The Indians
realized this. Besides, most of them were pleased
to see him again and the old chief was honestly
delighted.

The friendliness lasted for another month.
By the end of that time the Iroquois had done
some thinking. "If many French people come to
live in this fort," they said, "they will buy all
the beaver pelts. We will be unable to stop them,
for we must go home to our distant villages before winter. But if the French get hold of these
skins, what will we have to trade to our friends,
the Dutch?"

There was only one answer to that question.
The French would have to be killed and their
fort pulled down. Just one thing stopped the
Iroquois from making the attack at once. Twelve
of their most important chiefs were in Quebec,
guests of the governor. These chiefs would be
promptly hung if Fort Onondaga was destroyed
by men of their own tribe.

The Iroquois considered further. They built

their village of wigwams close to the fort to make
sure the French did not escape. They went on
pretending to be great friends with Pierre and
his white companions. But Pierre soon found out
what was happening. No Indian was ever able
to fool him for long.

"My father," he said to the chief one day,
"your people wish to kill us, I think."

The old man nodded. "They will kill you in
the spring," he said calmly. "By then your
French brothers will have sent away our chiefs
who visit them in Quebec. We will no longer
fear revenge when that happens."

Now it became Pierre's turn to think. It was
January. The Indians would certainly attack in
less than three months' time. If the Frenchmen
in the fort wanted to escape, they would have to
do so as quickly as possible. There were not
enough canoes for the sixty Frenchmen and the
crowd of Huron women and children. But there
was no other way of escape except down the river
and across Lake Ontario.

"We must build boats," Pierre said to Father
Ragueneau, "flat, wide boats in which we can
load all our people and food for them. I will

think of a way to launch them without the Iroquois knowing anything about it."

A French carpenter began secretly building boats in a room inside the fort. One day an Indian who had listened to Father Ragueneau preaching caught the Frenchman at work. The brave fled in terror to the Iroquois tents outside.

"The French priest speaks of a great flood that once drowned all the world," he moaned. "His people build many large boats at this very moment. No doubt the priest has learned from Heaven that another flood will soon arrive. They wish to save themselves like him who was called Noah."

Pierre heard this story. Quickly he told the carpenter to build a wooden floor over the half-finished boats. When angry Iroquois chiefs arrived, wanting to know what was going on, they were shown into the room. A few canoes were being repaired there. There was a strangely high new floor, a lot of tools, and one or two half-sawed planks, but no boats! Only the canoes. The Iroquois went away, muttering unpleasant things about the warrior who had told them lies.

March arrived. The deep snow around the fort began to melt. Increasing heat from the sun was already softening the ice on the river and the lake. Nights were still deadly cold, but Pierre knew that spring would be here in a very few weeks. The Iroquois and Onondaga were daily growing more quarrelsome. Pierre was sure they would attack with the first warm weather.

One day Father Ragueneau had an accident. He fell down and broke his arm while crossing a stretch of ice. The poor man was carried to his bed, where he lay in pain, groaning loudly.

"Good!" said the Iroquois and Onondaga. "While the holy man is ill, the French will not try to leave the fort. They would not travel with one who is so sick. Nor would they let him remain here alone. Our young men can go hunting deer. They will return with fresh meat that will strengthen us. Then we will attack."

Large hunting parties from both tribes sallied forth into the forest. No one except Pierre knew that Father Ragueneau's apparent accident was just a good idea. There was nothing at all wrong with his arm. Pierre had wanted to get rid of the braves.

Pierre's next inspiration was even more brilliant. He went to see the sixty or seventy warriors who had remained in the village to keep an eye on the French.

"Come and feast with us," he invited them. "We wish to show our friendship for our Indian brothers."

No Indian ever refused an invitation to a feast. Besides, the Iroquois had been short of food during the winter and were really hungry. They appeared at the fort, smacking their lips as they sniffed the rich smells coming from the kitchen.

Pierre seated them all on the open patch of ground inside the fort. Evening had come but flaring pine torches threw a reddish light. Blazing bonfires kept away the cold.

When the Iroquois and Onondaga had taken their places, sixty Frenchmen started bringing on the food. Dish after dish was set in front of the Indians, who stuffed themselves as fast as they could. "Ho!" they grunted approvingly. "Ho! What fine food!"

There were piled heaps of roasted corn with maple syrup. There were freshly boiled fish from the lake, big juicy turtles, boiled fowls, ducks, a dozen wild geese, and mountains of venison. There were stuffed eels, two enormous barrels of cheese, jars of rancid butter, and roast turkeys. Loaves of bread, slabs of pastry, heaps of dried currants, bowl after bowl of thick broth arrived without pause.

"Ho!" the Iroquois tried to shout again, but their voices were somewhat muffled. "Ho! Ho!"

An hour later they were not shouting at all. Indian politeness required that no guest should stop eating as long as any food remained on the table. Each had to do his part until every dish was empty.

There was no sign that the French feast would ever come to an end. Fresh supplies kept pouring out of the kitchen in an overwhelming stream. The Indians found themselves being presented with platter after platter of rich meat and vegetables, or a pound of cheese, or a leg of pork.

The unfortunate Iroquois ate until their distended stomachs forced them to stop. They paused and then struggled to down a few more mouthfuls. They sweated profusely, their eyes rolled, and they became silent. Presently a few of them even gave up trying to be polite. They fell over on their backs and went to sleep; that is, they tried to go to sleep.

But now there appeared several Frenchmen carrying drums and bugles. They blew terrific screeches on the bugles and banged the drums as hard as they could. "We make music for your pleasure," Pierre said politely to the miserable sleepers as they struggled to sit up.

The fun went on for another hour. The drums thumped and boomed without stopping. The bugles never ceased their frightful din. The appalling noise hid the sounds made by the heavy boats as they were dragged out of the fort by the French and carried down to the river.

The Indians had all reached the stage when nothing, not even politeness, drums, or bugles, mattered any more. They were stretched on their backs, hands clasped over stuffed stomachs, trying to sleep in spite of the noise.

One by one the Frenchmen sneaked out of the fort. They took with them their weapons, blankets, and food for the trip. With them went the Huron women. Pierre was the last to leave. His final act was to catch the one remaining pig and

tie it by one leg to the rope that dangled from
the bell over the gate. Any brave who woke up
would hear the loud ringing of the bell as the
pig tried to escape. The Indian would go to sleep
again, blessing the kind French soldiers who
rang the bell as proof that they were keeping
watch while their guests slumbered.

The surface of the river was covered with big
chunks of ice. In some places they had frozen
together, forming a sheet of ice that stretched
from bank to bank. Slowly the boats made their
way downstream. Men stood in the bows, chopping with heavy axes.

The great clumsy boats and the canoes that
went with them reached Lake Ontario at last.
For days and nights the French rowed or sailed
across the lake. They cooked rough meals over
fires which they quickly put out, fearing that
the smoke might be seen by Indians. The
weather was bitterly cold the whole time. When
the party reached the rapids, several of the boats
nearly overturned. One canoe actually did upset,
drowning two Frenchmen and a Huron. They
were the only people lost during the escape. The
rest of the fleet swept downstream with mus-

keteers standing guard while other men paddled or rowed.

On April 17, 1658, Three Rivers was sighted. The party had reached safety. They all owed their lives to one man, young Pierre Radisson.

## Chapter Five

## *RUNNING THE*
## *FUR BLOCKADE*

A<small>FTER</small> his escape from Fort Onondaga, Pierre became the hero of Three Rivers.
A less daring man would have been content with
such a reputation. He would have settled down
to a safer life, feeling thankful that his scalp was
not dangling from an Iroquois tent pole. Pierre,
however, was only at the beginning of his adventures.

A few weeks after he got back to the settlement, the governor of Quebec sent for him.
"Two years have passed," said the governor,

"since any furs have reached us. Yet Indians tell us that the country beyond Lake Huron contains tribes with hundreds of pelts to sell. These tribes will not come down the river, for they fear the Iroquois war parties. We must have their furs. All Europe is eager to buy them. We need the money to keep our settlements in Canada prosperous."

"These matters I understand, sir," said Pierre, "but they do not concern me."

"They do now," replied the governor. "You are the man I have chosen to bring in those furs."

This was just the sort of dangerous mission that Pierre loved. He was being asked to go into unknown country and make friends with the tribes who lived there. He was to coax them into forming a fleet of fur-carrying canoes. Finally, he was to lead the fleet down the swift-flowing Ottawa River to Quebec.

He had run enough risks already to realize that if he were not killed by Indians, he was quite likely to get drowned in rapids, starve to death in a snowbound forest, or fall sick and die in a lonely camp. He had a very small chance of doing what the governor wanted. But Pierre, being the kind of man he was, promised to see what he could do.

Knowing that two Frenchmen together had a better chance than one of staying alive, he asked another wild and reckless fellow to go with him, a man named Médard Groseilliers, whom the English later nicknamed Mr. Gooseberry. He was a great hairy fellow who was about ten years older than Pierre. He had an enormous beard, slow but cunning wits, and the courage of a grizzly bear. He had been a sergeant in the French army, a river pilot in Canada, and had done more than his share of Indian fighting. He was one of the few Frenchmen in Canada who had the nerves and strength to go with Pierre on such a hard and risky journey.

There were, however, many other Frenchmen at Quebec who thought it would be fun to go on a fur-seeking expedition. If they found enough pelts, every man would return home a good deal richer than when he left. Forty aristocratic young gentlemen who had just arrived from France told Pierre they had decided to accompany him. Pierre stared at their smart clothes, their fine lace cuffs, and their powdered wigs.

He listened to their delicate accents, sniffed their perfume . . . and agreed. By all means they could go with him—at their own risk.

The party set off up the Ottawa River in canoes paddled by Indians who lived in the fur-bearing country and now wanted to go home. Pierre and Médard Groseilliers winked at one another and wisely "went in the boats of the wild men," as Pierre put it. They did not want to be too near their own countrymen in case there should be any fighting. The Indians were more used to such encounters and more likely to keep their heads.

It might have been thought that the young Frenchmen were setting off on a picnic. The sunlit forests, the clear blue river, and the sight of wild animals drinking at its edge excited them wildly. They sang songs, fired off their guns, and boasted from morning to night what they would do to any Iroquois war parties that came along.

They had their chance to show what they could do. One fine sunny morning they were paddling along in careless formation, canoes strung out all over the river. Without warning a roar of musket fire crashed out of the forest, followed by Iroquois yells. Bullets skipped off the water and smacked holes in the light canoes. The enemy Indians had arranged a perfect ambush.

The young men turned their canoes and fled downstream, and all the other canoes followed. There was no singing now. The party landed with trembling speed. Axes were tugged out of the baggage and everyone except Pierre and Médard began chopping down trees to make a rough fort. The Frenchmen sweated and shivered with fright. The ax handles blistered their smooth hands. Their fine white shirts were soiled and torn by the tree trunks they hastily hauled into position. Those Iroquois yells had put the fear of death into the young gentlemen.

The fort was built more quickly than most forts. Everyone hurried into it and prepared to fight. But the Iroquois did not attack; they were only a small war party. That night Pierre quietly told everyone to get back into the canoes. Some were no longer there to be told. Thirteen Frenchmen had disappeared in the wild excitement that followed the ambush. Some were killed; others had fled downstream as fast as they could plunge their paddles into the water. None of the thirteen was ever heard of again.

The other young men were no longer interested in the loads of trade goods they had brought with them. They left the bundles where they were and scrambled into the canoes. All night the fleet paddled upstream, taking care to move as quietly as possible. They landed at dawn to make a portage. The river was full of rapids at this point, and the party had to carry their canoes until they reached smooth water a mile higher up.

The Frenchmen found they were expected to carry heavy loads on their backs. Even worse, they had to trot in order to keep up with the Indians. Pierre and Médard managed without much trouble. Their unhappy companions were less fortunate. They stumbled in the bushes, and when they fell their loads fell with them, pounding the breath out of their bruised bodies. Rocks tore their shoes and scratched their feet. Swarms of mosquitoes and black flies bit their soft white skins.

Somehow the party managed to reach the upper end of the portage. There the young French-

men set down their loads and collapsed on top
of them. They told Pierre that not for all the
beaver pelts in Canada would they go one step
or one paddle thrust farther. They intended to
turn back to Quebec at once as fast as they could.
Never again would they move outside Quebec
unless it were to return, with the greatest of joy,
to the civilized life of France.

Pierre, trying hard not to laugh, let them go.
He, Médard Groseilliers, and forty Indians were
left. There was to be no turning back for any of
them.

Traveling by night, sleeping in the woods by
day, they went five hundred miles up the Ottawa
River. Time after time they had to land and
carry their canoes past rapids. In the darkness
they struck rocks that capsized the canoes. No
one dared to fire a musket for fear that prowling
Iroquois might hear the noise. Food ran short
and everyone hunted along the shore for small
minnows which they ate raw.

At last the river widened out. Over green
banks of reeds and between the trunks of mighty
trees, Pierre sighted the glistening blue waters of
Lake Nipissing. The surface of the water was

covered with ducks. Deer, so seldom hunted that they were not afraid of human beings, trotted down to the water's edge to stare timidly at the passing canoes. On the shores of this beautiful lake the ragged and exhausted men rested for several days.

All his life Pierre was more interested in seeing new places than in making money. This lovely stretch of country must be explored. The furs could wait. He and Médard were going to do a little wandering.

The people who write history sometimes still squabble about where Pierre actually went during the next year. His own famous account of his travels, which he called *Voyages,* is not of much use in settling the arguments. Pierre simply did not know what part of America he was in. No one had made a map of it yet. He writes about "a large island," "another lake," "a strait," and a tribe of Indians who bore the wonderful name of the Staring Hairs because they wore their hair "like a brush turned up." But none of these islands and straits had a name. So no one knows exactly where Pierre went.

It is fairly certain that he and Médard paddled

down French River into Georgian Bay, which
lies on the north side of Lake Huron. There
they turned westward and went through Mackinac Strait into Lake Michigan. Following its
shore, they discovered the Fox River. Unknown
rivers fascinated Pierre. He paddled up it, down
the Wisconsin River, and so came to the wide
waters of the Mississippi. He may have reached
the Missouri River as well. Certainly he knew
all about these waters. He mentions that the
Mississippi flows into the Gulf of Mexico. If
Médard had not been there to stop him, Pierre
would probably have ended up somewhere off
the coast of Florida in his endless desire to find
out where rivers went.

The two explorers made friends with a tribe
living on Prairie Island in the Mississippi. They
settled down for a rest in the village, but before
long they were disturbed once more by the Iroquois. A war party had been scouting along the
banks of the Mississippi, killing a few Indians
here and there, stirring up trouble as usual.

Pierre liked the tribe he and Médard were living with. He did not want to see them attacked
by these savages from the Mohawk. He made up

a small war party of his own, placed himself and Médard at its head, and marched off after the Iroquois. He found them one evening when they were just sitting down to a meal round their fire. None of them ever lived to eat the food. The two Frenchmen and their Indian friends shot every single brave. After that they marched back to their island and spent the next three days feasting and singing.

Pierre still had no idea where he was or that he and Médard were very nearly the first Europeans to see the great Mississippi. Only one other Frenchman had ever come beyond Lake Huron before.

They spent the winter on Prairie Island. When spring came, they went up the lake again, making friends with other Indian tribes on the way. The wonderful crops and fruit which they saw growing beside every village continued to amaze and delight Pierre. He took pleasure in describing all the different kinds of food he tasted, the great size of the fish he caught in Lake Michigan, and how the Indians cooked them. Pierre loved that part of America. Its milder climate and friendly tribes were much to his liking after the cold country and savage Indians near the St. Lawrence. No wonder he and Médard spent another winter there, this time at Green Bay near the mouth of Lake Michigan.

Pierre realized when the second spring arrived that he and Médard would have to start hurrying. The governor in Quebec would be growing impatient. The explorers had not been wasting their time while they lived among the Indians. Their load of goods had disappeared, but in a hut near their own, glossy beaver pelts were piled from floor to roof. Moreover, they had made friends with half a dozen tribes round the lake. The men of these tribes promised to form a fleet, run the risk of encountering the Iroquois on the Ottawa River, and bring to Quebec thousands and thousands of pelts. Pierre was delighted. Not only would he and Médard make a great deal of money out of their own furs, but the little French settlements would also prosper.

One day in spring the Indians told Pierre that they had changed their minds. If Frenchmen wanted furs, they would have to come and get them on Lake Michigan. The Ottawa River was too dangerous.

Pierre called the headmen of the tribes together. While they squatted on the ground, he stood and argued with them.

"What use are beaver skins to you?" he fiercely demanded. "Will you kill your enemies, the Iroquois, by smothering them in pelts? No! For that you need sharp axes, knives of bright steel, and muskets such as mine. These weapons lie ready at Quebec. They are yours in return for the skins. Do not be afraid, my brothers. Come with my friend and me."

Pierre was a good talker. He made the Indians feel ashamed of themselves. Several hundred of them stepped into canoes a few days later. In each canoe glistened a load of beautiful furs. The tribes were ready to encounter the hostile Iroquois.

Across Lake Michigan they went, into Lake Huron. Soon they were streaming up French River into the serene beauty of Lake Nipissing. There they halted and prepared for the most dangerous part of the voyage, down the Ottawa River. Muskets were loaded, bowstrings were examined, quivers of arrows laid ready in each canoe. Pierre then led his fleet into the entrance

to the river. In another canoe beside him sat the
bearded Médard, musket resting on his knees,
sharp eyes watching the forest ahead.

Nothing happened during the first few days.
But along the banks the fur-runners discovered
blackened patches of ground where Iroquois
campfires had burned. Pierre knew these warriors were still somewhere in the district. He
sent three light canoes, paddled by strong young
Indians, ahead of the main party. When a portage had to be made, those who carried bales of
fur were guarded by others armed with bows
and arrows or precious muskets.

Late one afternoon the scouts came tearing
upstream as fast as they could move. Around the
next bend they had sighted sixteen canoes filled
with Iroquois. This was a bigger war party than
even Pierre had expected.

The fur-runners grew terrified. They were
afraid of fighting a big battle with the Iroquois.
They wanted to escape upriver as fast as they
could, hoping that the Iroquois would not follow. But Pierre and the reckless Médard had a
different idea. Already they had brought the
furs a thousand miles. Quebec lay only a few

days' journey ahead. Not for all the Indians in America were they going to turn back now.

The two Frenchmen bullied, coaxed, and argued with the Indians. As usual, they got their own way. Piles of furs were hastily erected in the bows of the canoes as protection against flying arrows and musket balls. Pierre and Médard formed the fleet into line. They placed themselves in the center canoes in the front rank. Those Indians who had muskets took up positions on either side of them. Singing, shouting, and yelling their war cries, the fur-runners swept down the river toward the waiting enemy.

The Iroquois heard the approaching roar of voices. This was something new. Generally it was they who attacked others; now they themselves were being attacked. Suddenly they fled for the shore, ran their canoes up on dry land, and formed a line along the water's edge.

The fur fleet came roaring round the bend. In each canoe Indians were peering along the sights of their muskets. The grim figures of Pierre and Médard were in the middle. Each of them was holding a gun and preparing to take aim.

"Do not fire," Pierre had ordered the Indians, "until you hear the sound of my musket. Then press your triggers as quickly as you can."

The Iroquois were badly shaken. They began a wild volley of shots before the leading canoes were in range. They were struggling to reload when there came two loud bangs. The reports were followed by a roaring volley and the thin whistling of flying arrows. That was enough for the Iroquois. Those who could still run, did. Behind them on the beach they left the dead and wounded. A dozen of their braves had died in a few seconds.

The fur fleet went on. Grimly Pierre and his companions reloaded their guns or chose fresh arrows.

Three days later the scouts came tearing upstream again. They had seen a few Iroquois in the distance. There might be another war party on the bank. This time Pierre tried a new kind of attack. His Indians landed. Two hundred and fifty of them sneaked through the thick forest. A mile farther on they caught sight of a big party of Iroquois. A deadly game of hide-and-seek began among the trees. Those who hid badly

or too late paid with their lives for the mistake. The Iroquois retreated, leaving nine dead warriors behind them, and hurriedly built a fort of fallen tree trunks. Behind its walls they waited to beat off the fur-runners' next attack.

Pierre and his men built themselves another fort within a hundred yards of the Iroquois. They were attacked several times before they had finished. Each time they drove off their attackers with gunfire.

The two parties sat in their forts throughout the night. Pierre had grown impatient by the time morning came. Getting those furs to Quebec was the most important thing in his life. He was determined that nothing should stop him.

The Iroquois screeched with alarm when suddenly they saw Indians coming out of the other fort. Parties of four, five, and six men were rolling big bundles of fur in front of them as they advanced. The skins acted as perfect shields against arrows and lead shot. There was nothing the war party could shoot at. In a few minutes they would be attacked by several hundred fighting men armed with axes, guns, tomahawks, and knives.

The Iroquois ran for their lives. They left in such a hurry that their baggage fell into the hands of Pierre's men. This extra loot was stowed in the canoes.

The fur fleet went on. Two days later they came to a clearing in the forest where there had been a tremendous fight between Iroquois and Frenchmen. A splintered and bullet-pierced wooden fort stood back a little distance from the river. The tree-trunk walls were blackened with fire and bristling with broken arrow shafts. The surrounding grass had been beaten flat by the tread of running feet. Bits of broken weapons, blood-stained feathers, and torn moccasins were scattered everywhere. From near-by trees hung the bodies of seventeen Frenchmen. Every one of them had been scalped. In the cold ashes of huge bonfires lay the bones of other men.

Pierre found out later that he had been gazing at the scene of one of the most famous fights that ever took place in Canada between Frenchmen and Iroquois. In the spring of that year 1660, French settlers had heard terrible news. Their treaty with the Iroquois was to be completely broken. One thousand warriors were coming down the Ottawa River to wipe out every Frenchman living along the St. Lawrence.

A young Frenchman named Adam Daulac went to see the governor of Montreal. "Let me choose men, sir," he begged, "who will go up the river with me and meet the Iroquois. The lesson we will give them may change their minds about attacking our settlements. They will learn how Frenchmen can fight."

The worried governor agreed. Daulac found sixteen young Frenchmen (some were only nineteen years old) to go with him. Ten friendly and gallant Hurons asked to join the party. The little band set off in canoes up the Ottawa River. When they knew they were near the Iroquois, they landed and built the fort that Pierre had seen. The Frenchmen had brought with them a load of muskets and pistols and several blunderbusses—bell-mouthed guns which fired heavy charges of iron fragments. They were also well stocked with powder and shot. Inside the fort they awaited the Iroquois attack.

Four days later several hundred warriors came running up from the river, yelling and shouting as they ran. They were met by a roar of gunfire.

Dozens of them were killed or slashed by the wicked scraps of iron hurtling out of the blunderbusses. The Iroquois fled back to their canoes, howling with disappointed rage. During the next four days they made one attack after another. The weary Frenchmen, blackened by smoke, their eyes red from exhaustion and lack of sleep, kept up their heroic defense. Water gave out and the young men dug a well inside the fort. Not until it was too late did the well begin to fill.

On the morning of the fifth day, the Iroquois made a wild charge on the fort from several different directions at once. They reached the walls, swarmed over them, and jumped down inside. Daulac and his friends dropped their empty muskets and grabbed swords and pistols. One by one they were killed, but many more Iroquois died with them.

The French settlements were never attacked. "If seventeen young men fight like this," grumbled the Indian chiefs, "how will two thousand of their fathers fight from behind strong walls? It is wiser to leave the settlements alone."

It was also thanks to Adam Daulac that Pierre had managed to fight his way so far down the river. Many of the Iroquois had gone south in disgust. Only the last war parties were left to stop the fur fleet from reaching Quebec. But if Pierre had come down the Ottawa a few days earlier, he would have met a thousand Iroquois in good fighting form. Not even the two tough Frenchmen and their followers could have dealt with all that number.

At last they sighted Montreal. Cheering Frenchmen raced out of the town and lined the river banks as the fast-moving fleet of canoes swept downstream with flashing paddles. The settlers knew that those big bales of furs meant wealth for the little colony. French Canada had been saved from ruin for another year. The loudest cheer of all was for Pierre Radisson and Médard Groseilliers. They were still leading the fleet. Muskets were balanced across their knees. They were ragged and their long hair was matted and greasy from gun smoke. The bows of many of the canoes showed white splinters where musket balls or arrowheads had torn the frail bark. But it was a proud fleet that came sweeping toward the land, a fleet that had fought and won its right to descend the Ottawa River.

The fur-runners rested for two days at Montreal. Then they paddled on to Three Rivers. Here they picked up an escort, a heavy little sailing boat with three small cannon mounted on her tiny deck.

Below Three Rivers another Iroquois war party made an attack. They came within range of the cannon. Iron shot smashed their canoes and hurled the crews into the water. The survivors paddled or swam back to the forest-lined shore. That spring was a most unlucky one for the Iroquois. They had earned the lesson they were being taught.

At last the fur fleet rode into sight of Quebec. The amazed and delighted inhabitants saluted them with thundering guns and the batteries of the fort and of three ships at anchor in the river. Those ships would have gone back to France without beaver skins if Pierre's expedition had not arrived. He and Médard and their crews were banqueted for five days. The governor bestowed gifts upon them and provided two small vessels to convey them back home.

*Chapter Six*

## THE BAY
## OF THE NORTH

THE furs sold at high prices. Pierre and Médard had their pockets full of good gold pieces. Both of them decided to rest awhile at Three Rivers before starting off on another trip to the wilds. Meanwhile Médard bought himself a pleasant little farm on the shore of the St. Lawrence. He knew that it meant security for his old age. Pierre could have bought land also, but he was not eager to settle down. His wandering life had made him restless. He

113

wanted to go back on the trail where he would meet other tribes and find new country.

He had not done too badly as an explorer. The French priests were delighted with the mass of information he gave them about the almost unknown Lake Michigan. Carefully they wrote down all he told them about the beautiful country along its shores and about his trip to the Mississippi. They would now be able to fill in portions of their maps that had been left blank for lack of information. For the next fifty years other explorers planned their own journeys with the help of these maps. Some of the men must have wondered, perhaps a little enviously, how a young man of twenty-four had managed to do so much and not get killed in the process of doing it.

During those cold winter months at Three Rivers, Pierre and Médard talked quietly in front of their fire. A few words used by their Indian friends on Lake Michigan had stuck in their minds. "The bay whose waters are salt," the Indians had said, "the Bay of the North."

The mysterious Bay of the North was to become to Pierre what the Holy Grail had been to the knights of King Arthur—an object of arduous search.

Northern Canada was a vast country of forests and lakes. No man could say where its coast began or ended. But Pierre wanted to know. An idea had occurred to him. Somewhere in that cold and lonely north the sea might wash against the land. What else could those words mean, "whose waters are salt"? Carrying furs down the Ottawa River was a slow and risky business. If the sea lay to the north, furs could be taken up there and loaded into ships that would go straight to Europe. There were no Iroquois to worry about in the north. Perhaps it might not be as far from Lake Michigan to the sea as it was from Lake Michigan to Quebec. Pierre made up his mind to go searching now for the Bay of the North.

Both he and Médard Groseilliers had learned the Indian trick of silence in order to keep a secret. They never said a word about their plan. They decided to set off in the spring of 1661 and try to find the bay for themselves.

Early in April, Pierre went to the governor of Quebec and asked for permission to make another trip. No one was supposed to leave the settlements without leave.

The governor who had asked Pierre to bring furs to Quebec had gone back to France. The dishonest and unpopular Vicomte d'Argenson was now governor. "I'll give you permission to go," he said to Pierre, "if you'll give me half the money you get for the furs you bring back. And to make sure you don't try to swindle me, two of my men will go along with you."

Pierre replied, "You can come with us yourself, sir, but we will not take two of your clerks in our canoes."

The governor had no wish to lose his scalp to savages. If Pierre would not take the two men with him, then he could not have permission to make the trip.

Pierre and Médard returned to Three Rivers in a defiant frame of mind. Most of the Indians who had come from Lake Michigan had already gone home, but thirty of them were still living with the French. They would make pleasant company for a voyage up the Ottawa River. If d'Argenson would not give permission, the voyage would have to be made without it.

One night Pierre, Médard, and a Frenchman called François sneaked out of Three Rivers in a couple of canoes. Everyone knew that the Quebec governor had forbidden Pierre to leave the settlement. A sentry on the stockade spotted the black shadows of the canoes as they glided out into the St. Lawrence. He threw up his musket. "Who goes there?" he bawled.

A deep laugh came back across the water. "It is I, Groseilliers. With me is Pierre Radisson."

The sentry lowered his gun and grinned into the darkness. "Good luck, my friends," he shouted. "May God bring you back in safety."

The Lake Michigan Indians were waiting a short distance upstream, their canoes packed with the loads Médard had given them to carry earlier that day. The two parties joined up and headed for the Ottawa River. There was no time to waste; summer had come. Pierre wanted to be settled in some Indian camp before winter.

François was of little use on the trip. He spent much of his time wondering what would happen if the Iroquois caught him. Pierre described exactly what would happen to him and François became extremely nervous. A few days later the party, having seen Iroquois canoes in the distance, hastily landed, hid their canoes, and ran into the forest. François ran so far that he had not returned when the Indians with whom he was sharing a canoe were ready to go on with the voyage. They left him behind in disgust and did not tell Pierre until several hours later. By that time it was much too late to do anything about it.

François was unusually lucky. Another party of Frenchmen and Indians happened to come past a few days later. They saw the wretched fellow sitting on the bank eating berries. He had a musket on his back but did not know how to fire it. The newcomers picked him up, fed him, and dropped him off at Three Rivers. Governor d'Argenson, already angry with Pierre for going without leave, had François locked up in jail. The goodhearted settlers, considering that the miserable young man had suffered enough without this extra punishment, broke into the jail and let him out.

By this time Pierre had run up against the Iroquois again. When his party landed to make a portage, they discovered an Iroquois fort blocking the road by which they would have to return to the river. Pierre went and had a look at the fort. He was nearly shot, but the Indians recognized him as a Frenchman. The tremendous fight Daulac and his sixteen companions had made was still an unpleasant memory to the Iroquois. Having no desire to attack any more Frenchmen for some time, they hurriedly left the fort and hid in the forest.

More serious trouble was encountered when Pierre was fifty miles farther up the river. His fleet met a small war party coming down and a few shots were fired by both sides. Three Iroquois were killed, but Pierre's men were not even injured. Both parties made for the shore. The Iroquois took shelter in an old fort on the bank. Pierre decided this was the time to teach them a lesson.

When dusk fell he and his companions sneaked towards the Iroquois fort. The braves heard them coming and began firing wildly into the darkness, but no one was hit. Pierre crawled to the wall of the fort without being seen and hurled over it a contraption he had made during the afternoon—a little barrel full of gunpowder and bits of iron. The fuse leading to the powder was already lighted.

A few seconds later there was a colossal red flash and an explosion that echoed through the night. Iroquois, yelling in terror, poured out of the fort and ran wildly into the forest. They left behind them twelve dead and five wounded.

Pierre and his men went on to peaceful Lake Nipissing and camped there for a few days. They were all in need of food and rest after the perilous journey up the river. They shot deer and caught as many fish as they wanted. Summer was ending in a spell of beautiful weather and for nearly a fortnight they drowsed lazily in the sunshine.

By the beginning of October, Pierre was sailing along the north shore of Lake Huron. At Sault Sainte Marie the Indians who had accompanied the explorers were welcomed by the families they had left eighteen months earlier, and some of them left Pierre's party.

Fifteen miles above Sault Sainte Marie the smooth blue waters of the strait widened out into the great expanse of Lake Superior. Pierre was the first white man to see it. He paddled along the southern shore, admiring the superb forests that swept down to the water and observing with his keen eyes the signs of plenty of beaver.

The tribes living beside the lake were friendly. Night after night the party camped on the shore without fear of attack. They swam in the cold water, ate as much venison and bear steak as they wanted, and slept peacefully in their blankets under the clear light of the stars. No wonder Pierre described this country as the fairest he had seen in all his wanderings. He was in no hurry to end such a delightful stay. Not till the first frosts came did he start thinking about where he and Médard would spend the winter. They launched their canoes and sailed towards the west.

They saw many strange and wonderful sights during the next few weeks. There were places where the stones and rocks were almost entirely composed of copper—metal that would have been worth much money in Quebec or Europe. They paddled past a huge cliff rising sheer from the water whose face had been dyed red, blue, purple, and green by copper. It looked as if a

giant had playfully daubed paint of many colors
on it with a huge brush. They saw a strange
rock, carved by thousands of years of rain and
wind until it looked like a devil pointing his
hand over the lake. Later on they beheld the
entrance to a vast cave. In rough weather the
waves rushed into it with great violence, forcing
air and spray upward through hundreds of holes
in the stone. The roaring and trumpeting, so
the Indians said, could be heard three or four
miles away.

At last they came to the western end of the
lake. This was the land of the Cree Indians. It
was from the Crees whom he had met on Lake
Michigan that Pierre had first heard of the Bay
of the North. Many of the natives were there
to welcome the Frenchmen as brothers. They
smiled with pleasure when Pierre gave them
presents he had brought from Three Rivers,
among them a couple of good pistols for their
chief.

"Come and spend the winter in our village,"
said the Crees. "The distance is not great, a mere
four days' journey on foot."

Pierre agreed. Only one thing worried him.

He and Médard had brought a great quantity of trade goods from Three Rivers. Neither of them liked the idea of carrying such treasures into even a friendly village.

"Do not wait for us," said Pierre to the Crees. "Soon we will follow you."

As soon as the Indians had gone, Pierre and Médard dug a deep hole in the ground and lowered the precious goods into it, shoveling the earth back on top. They kept out only as many articles as they could carry on their backs.

Some of the Crees were camped a little distance inland. They had decided to wait for the explorers. "Where are all the fine things you carried?" they asked with surprise.

"I have sunk them into the lake," said Pierre in a solemn voice. "The god of our people will watch over them and let the water ruin none."

The Crees were satisfied. They led the way over forest-covered hills and along unknown rivers, the region that is now the state of Wisconsin. Finally they reached a beautiful little lake. On its far side was their village. They ferried the Frenchmen over in canoes. Long before they reached the other side, their fellow villagers were lining the banks, singing and shouting cries of welcome. A lane was made for the explorers between lines of excited Indians. They strode along it, feeling like gods among men. Never before had they received such a welcome.

They brought out some of the gifts they had carried in their heavy packs, presenting a fine hunting knife to a chief, a sword to his brother, and an ax to another important Cree. Nor had Pierre forgotten the Indian women. To some of them he gave attractive combs, looking glasses, a few cheap bottles of perfume, and bead necklaces. Dark-eyed children were delighted when he handed them small brass rings, lengths of gay ribbon, and little French dolls.

It was November when the Frenchmen reached the village and winter was closing down on the land. Pierre found himself a home with one family, Médard with another. There were sons and daughters in both families, whom the explorers adopted as their brothers and sisters. Pierre and Médard settled down for the winter in the smoky, dirty huts. They were content. The people around them knew the secret of the unknown Bay of the North.

*Chapter Seven*

## THE WINTER
## OF DEATH

Whirling blizzards drove southward across Lake Superior. Snowdrifts piled higher and higher round the village where Pierre and his partner shivered over tiny fires. Freezing winds screamed through the forests, and great trees groaned and split from the terrible cold.

The explorers were used to icy weather, but even Pierre was alarmed by the beginning of that winter. Never had he seen anything like it. The cold worked its way into the squalid wigwams. Water only a few feet away from the fire

froze within an hour. The Indians wrapped
themselves in beaver cloaks or blankets and
silently prepared to endure the misery they knew
was coming.

Food was short; stocks of fuel were low. During the warm summer months, Indians seldom
thought of making ready for winter. They set
aside small stocks of dried meat and corn and
left their womenfolk to gather what fuel they
thought they would need. But there was no careful planning. An Arctic winter such as this was
bound to cause suffering and death.

The village warriors became alarmed. They
put on snowshoes and set out to hunt game.
Pierre and Médard went with them. The men
plodded into the frozen woods with muskets and
bows, ready to kill any animal, big or small.
Things went well for a week or two. There was
plenty of game sheltering among the trees. Médard shot a caribou; Pierre brought down a
moose. The Crees killed a few bears. The deep
snow made it difficult for the animals to escape
the hunters. A man on snowshoes could move
faster than a deer floundering through drifts up
to its belly.

The village ate well for another three weeks. Day after day the men came home with enough to keep their families well fed. Bear meat was especially welcome. The fat it contained could be melted down and stored in jars.

Gradually, however, the weather became even worse. Soon it was impossible to reach the forest. The falling snow froze on the ground and its surface became too slippery even for snowshoes. Game, frightened by daily attacks, moved deeper into the woods. The hunters began returning to the village with nothing to show for their efforts. Still the snow fell and the temperature dropped.

One day came a further misfortune. A large band of Ottawa Indians floundered into the village, some with wives and children. The hungry Crees found themselves expected to provide food for an extra two hundred people. The Ottawas had brought nothing with them except their weapons. They were a stupid tribe without sense enough to remain in their own villages during the winter. Pierre, like every other Frenchman, detested them. "They are the cursedest and cowardliest people that I have seen among all the nations I have met," he wrote later.

Cowardly or not, the Ottawas were as hungry as everyone else. Hunger makes anyone forget his fears. Besides, the Ottawa warriors outnumbered the Crees two to one. They felt strong enough to start bullying the villagers. Like a pack of miserable, treacherous hounds, they crawled from door to door, shouting for food as they went. They even robbed small children of their tiny rations.

Soon there was nothing left to eat. Hunting was still impossible. The Crees began to die of starvation. Old people were the first to go, then children and the sick. In nearly every hut could be heard the sounds of sobbing and crying. Faces became like skulls, hollow-cheeked, with great staring eyes. Families softened deerskin in boiling water so that they might chew the hide in the hope of finding nourishment. Warriors even ate their bowstrings.

Things were as bad for Pierre and his companion as they were for everyone else. At first they tried digging down through deep snow and frozen soil with their hunting knives, trying to find a few tender roots. They had to give up. Even the mighty Médard was so weak that he could not work for more than a few minutes at a time. Next they stripped bark from trees, boiled it, strained off the water, and ate the sticky mass that was left. Between two flat stones they ground up leather moccasins, softened the fragments in water and swallowed them.

Then came what seemed like a miracle. The weather turned milder for a whole week. Once again it was possible to reach the forest. But the task of walking so far was more than most of the Indians could manage. Some of them collapsed on the snow and lay there until they died. Their companions lacked the strength to haul them back to the village. The luckier ones reached the trees and found among them bones and skulls of animals they had killed during the summer. They staggered back, hugging their treasures. Men and women ground the bones to powder, mixed it with water, and swallowed the brew. Then the terrible frost closed down again. It became impossible to go outside of the huts. More of the villagers died.

One day two Sioux warriors reached the camp. They carried a small supply of rations on their backs, but only enough to last them a few days.

With them came a dog. Pierre was unable to take his eyes off the scraggy animal. He offered a pair of muskets, a bale of beaver skins, several steel knives—nearly everything he had—in exchange for the dog. The Sioux would not sell. They regarded the poor brute as a future meal for themselves.

Pierre knew the hut in which the Sioux were staying. He crawled towards it for several nights in succession and sat waiting in the snow. One night the dog came out. Pierre softly whistled and the animal came towards him. Turning back to his own hut, Pierre quietly called the dog to follow. At the same time he drew a sharp-pointed knife from his belt.

Pierre's Indian family ate well for the next few days. When they had devoured every scrap of meat, they made soup from the bones. Later they ground the bones to a fine powder and ate them. This extra food kept them alive. No one died in Pierre's hut throughout the winter. Médard's family was just as lucky.

The raging cold began to disappear at the end of January. Out of the huts came thin, staggering figures. Bony fingers clasped bows and spears.

Men set off towards the woods with awful hunger in their faces. There must be game somewhere. Better to die searching for it than starve to death in icy huts.

They found deer. A herd had strayed close to the village. Deep in snow, they were unable to flee when they saw the hunger-mad Indians lurching towards them. The hunters killed animal after animal. They drank the blood and ate warm raw meat. Four or five men shared the task of hauling each carcass back to the village. Several days passed before the Crees had eaten enough to satisfy their hunger. Only then did the women pause to cook the meat. Those deer saved what was left of the village.

The explorers had forgotten about the Bay of the North for the time being. They had even lost their interest in pelts. Until the middle of February they stayed with their families, eating from morning to night, and warming their cold bodies in the slowly growing warmth of the sun.

The two Sioux whose dog Pierre had eaten departed for their own country farther west. They told their tribe that two Frenchmen were staying in the Cree village. At the end of February a large party of Sioux chieftains and their followers reached the settlement. They had come to see the white men.

Pierre was delighted. The Sioux were the strongest and most important tribe of the West. Their country was full of beaver. If he could make friends with this tribe, Pierre would be able to get thousands and thousands more pelts than he had expected.

The Sioux were just as anxious to make friends with the Frenchmen. They wanted muskets. Other tribes were beginning to use these weapons and the Sioux were determined to have them too. They knew they could get plenty of arms from the French in exchange for beaver skins.

Pierre and the Sioux did everything possible to show their friendship for one another. The Indians gave beautiful robes of deerskin to the Frenchmen. They prepared tremendous feasts. After eating they lighted peace pipes and all sat smoking for hours at a time. Once they threw a few handfuls of tobacco into a blazing fire, the highest sign of friendship they could give.

Pierre had been waiting for this tobacco-throwing act. He wanted to show the Sioux that the French were a hardy race. From his tobacco pouch he produced a small roll of what he said was European tobacco. Actually the roll contained gunpowder. He threw it casually on the fire.

By the time the noise and sparks had died down and the smoke had drifted away, the Sioux were running madly out of the village, scared out of their wits. Pierre rushed after them and caught up with them just as they were diving into the forest. They would agree to return only after Pierre had promised that never again would he put quite so much European "tobacco" on the flames.

Pierre admired the Sioux more than any other tribe he had ever met. They were a fine, clever race of warriors. They wore beautiful deerskin robes, ornamented with brightly colored designs. Their bows and arrows were perfectly made. Their polite manners and dignity were a pleasant change after the savage habits of most other tribes.

The feasting went on for several days. The Sioux sang songs of welcome. Pierre sang back to them. The Sioux threw more tobacco on the fire. Pierre threw minute quantities of gunpowder. The Sioux showed how they could fight with their swords. Médard Groseilliers, an expert swordsman, drew his own blade and displayed more tricks than they had ever dreamed of. The Indians gave more presents and received in return knives, axes, daggers, beads, and paint. To the joy of the Sioux's leader, Pierre gave him one of his few remaining pistols.

The Sioux asked the Frenchmen to visit their country, a hundred and fifty miles to the west. Pierre accepted. He and Médard tramped across wild, beautiful country that had never before been explored by white men. They stayed with the friendly Sioux a month, taking part in dancing, feasting, and games. When they left to return east, they knew that they could trade with the Sioux for every beaver pelt they had. If only they could find that Bay of the North, they could send a wonderful stream of furs in ships to Europe. But the bay had still to be found. Pierre was not sure yet if it really was part of the ocean.

When he got back to the Cree village, he had a fright. The Ottawas had departed for Lake

Superior. They would be bad people to have around when the explorers started digging up the cache of trade goods they had left there.

Pierre and Médard started off for the lake at once, each of them pulling a sled loaded with beaver pelts. They decided to cross the ice rather than take the longer way round by the shore. The frozen surface of the lake was gradually melting and bitterly cold water lay on it. Pierre and Médard often had to wade in it up to their knees. They were numb and shaking with cold before they had gone very far. Soon they found it difficult to walk. They would have turned back, but the thought of the prowling Ottawas drove them on.

The shore was still five miles away when Pierre fell down. His frozen legs would no longer carry him. Médard picked him up and laid him on top of his sled. Then he managed to walk the remaining distance to the land, hauling his own sled after him. By chance he came to the spot where the Ottawas had camped. He begged the Indians to go out on the ice and rescue his partner.

The worthless Ottawas refused. Médard dared

not go back himself. He was tired out and, besides, he knew that if he left his load of furs,
the Indians would steal the lot. But the ice was
melting steadily; Pierre was in danger of being
drowned. At last Médard succeeded in bribing
the Ottawas with presents. They set out, grum-
bling, and dragged Pierre to safety.

A fortnight passed before Pierre was able to
move. Médard looked after him tenderly for the
first week, then was obliged to leave him. Neither explorer could rest easy until the buried
trade goods were dug up and placed under
guard in canoes or on sleds. Médard was going to
take care of them. Pierre was to join him as soon
as he could walk.

Some days later a party of Ottawas decided
to make a trip in the direction Pierre wanted to
go. He staggered out of his hut, picked up his
pack, musket, and cooking pot, and went along
with them. The trail led across rough country
still deep in snow. Pierre was too weak to keep
up with the Indians. He fell down again before
he had gone very far. The painful cramp in his
legs had returned and a new misery had come
upon him—he had gone snow-blind.

The Ottawas helped themselves to Pierre's musket and pack, allowing him only a small quantity of dried meat and a packet of corn. Then they went on their way, leaving him to die.

Pierre lay in the snow until he felt stronger. At last he picked himself up and tried to move forward. Afternoon had come and the glare on the snow was not so dazzling as it had been earlier in the day. He could see just well enough to walk. He took the path that he guessed would lead him to the cache. Not for one second did he think of returning to the Ottawa camp. He was determined to reach Médard or die on the way. He groped along until it grew dark, when he made himself a fire with a few sticks that he found.

Next morning he went on again. His legs were full of pain, but he was able to keep them moving. Every now and then he fell down, but each time he got up again and plodded on. He walked in wide circles when the snow blindness was severe. Often he lost his sense of direction. One night he found a ruined hut. He went in, made himself a roaring fire, stripped off his wet garments, and lay down to sleep in a warm cor-

ner. The roof caught fire while he was asleep.
Pierre woke up to find crackling flames leaping
all round him. He grabbed his clothes, threw
them into the darkness outside, and stumbled
out of the hut. The biting cold made him gasp
with pain. Half-naked, half-blind, and weak
from hunger, Pierre went crawling across the
snow, groping for the garments he must find in
order to keep alive. He found them one by one.
By morning he was fully dressed and staggering
along the trail.

Near the end of his dreadful journey Pierre
met an Indian who had seen him at the Cree
village. The Indian took Pierre's pack, sat down,
and ate the last rations it contained.

When he had finished, he looked at Pierre
and grinned. "Are you hungry, O friend?" he
asked.

Pierre was starved but his pride would not
let him say so. "I am well fed," he answered.

The Indian laughed. He opened his own pack
and brought out lumps of good red meat, a stone
jar of bear's fat, a handful of freshly cooked
corn. He thrust all the food at Pierre. "Eat," he
said.

Pierre ate. He ate everything he was given. That meal saved his life.

The Indian had news of Médard. He had seen a white man, a big Frenchman with a fine beard, camped beside the lake. How far? As far as a man could walk in half a day.

They parted. Feeling stronger after his meal, Pierre trudged along. He passed through a wood, stumbled down a long rocky slope, and began groping his way across open country. He heard shouts long before he could see who was calling. But he knew the voice. Médard, his faithful companion, was running towards him.

The journey to the cache should have taken three days. Pierre had just managed to get there and it had taken him nine days.

## Chapter Eight

## THE GOVERNOR'S REVENGE

PIERRE lay on a couch of beaver skins for three days. Warmth from a steadily blazing fire and plenty of good food cured him quickly. He watched while Médard dug up the trade goods and made sure that none of them had been damaged.

The partners began making plans to find their way to the Bay of the North. Near their camp was a party of Crees. The Indians said that in a few days' time they were going to travel northward. They would spend the summer

144

hunting and fishing along the shores of the lake whose waters were salt. They did this every year when the plains became hot and game scarce. They invited the white men to go with them.

Pierre was eager to get started. Now they would not have to go wandering across country by themselves, hoping to pick up news or find trails that might lead them to the bay. This was their chance to go directly to it.

They were packing when a crowd of Ottawas arrived and made camp a short distance away. Pierre was disturbed. The Ottawas were a jealous and suspicious lot. They would dislike intensely the idea of the Frenchmen going with the Crees, for they were quite aware that Pierre was looking for all the beaver pelts he could get. The Ottawas wanted the skins for themselves. Lazy and good-for-nothing though they were, they picked up a few hundred pelts every year which they traded to the Iroquois for iron kettles, good French muskets, and brightly colored cloth.

Pierre spoke quietly to the Crees. "Cross the lake in your canoes now," he said. "Wait for us on the other side. We will follow as soon as we can escape without letting the Ottawas see us go."

The Crees grinned. They had not forgotten how the Ottawas had behaved during the winter in their village. That night they departed after saying good-by to the Frenchmen in voices loud enough to be heard by the Ottawas in their camp.

When darkness fell, Pierre and Médard went into their hut. They lay there until the sound of chattering voices in the Ottawa camp had died away. Then they silently got up. The Crees had given them a couple of big canoes which were on the shore only fifty yards away. The partners carried down load after load of pelts, trade goods, and weapons. Silently they climbed into the canoes and paddled out into the starlit darkness. No one saw them go. Not even a dog barked.

All that night the canoes made their way northward. The lake was covered with jagged blocks of ice which made haste dangerous. A hole might easily be made in the fragile little craft. At last the sky grew light and the sun came up. Resting on their paddles, the Frenchmen saw the north shore of Lake Superior ahead. Pine-covered hillsides rose from the water. A blue mist hung about the lower slopes. Moose and caribou, standing knee-deep in the silent water, stared fearlessly at the fleet of hovering canoes.

Pierre had no idea where the Crees might be. Finding their camp would perhaps be difficult. He and Médard talked it over while they cooked breakfast on the shore. They decided to put up sails in their canoes and cruise along the shore in the hope of sighting the Crees. All that day they sailed eastward, each sitting in the stern of his canoe and steering with a paddle. That night they camped. The next morning they pushed off again. Towards noon they observed smoke rising among the dark-green trees. The Crees saw them almost at the same time. Quickly they launched their own canoes and came paddling out to greet the visitors with cries of welcome.

"They suffered not that we trod on ground," Pierre wrote. "They carried us into the middle of their cottages in our own boats like a couple of cocks in a basket."

The Crees had only been waiting for the Frenchmen to arrive. Two days later the entire party packed up and took to the trail. After so many troubles—hunger, sickness, and danger— the partners thankfully realized that they were heading for the bay, that mysterious stretch of water which no European now in Canada had yet seen.

The party tramped through wild, empty country. For days at a time they saw no other Indians. They camped beside forest-ringed lakes at night and waded through fast-running rivers. Gullies had to be crossed and great forests passed. Still the Indians kept on. After traveling for many days, they came to the biggest river they had yet reached. The Crees said it flowed into the Bay of the North. For the rest of the journey they would walk along its bank.

No one quite knows at what point the explorers reached Hudson Bay, the name given by the English to the Bay of the North. Some say it was the Albany River they followed. Others declare it was the Moose River. Whatever route Pierre took, the day came when he stood at the edge of a wide gray stretch of water. Quickly he dipped his fingers and tasted them. The water was salt! This was the Bay of the North!

Pierre Radisson and Médard Groseilliers were the first men to discover the southern shore of Hudson Bay. Fifty years earlier Henry Hudson had sailed into the bay from the sea and lost his life doing it. But he knew nothing of where the bay ended. Pierre and Médard discovered that and, in so doing, discovered a way of reaching Hudson Bay from the rich fur country round Lake Superior. Theirs was the idea of shipping out furs by this northern sea rather than taking them down the Ottawa River. From now on many people who had not even thought about Canada before became interested in it.

Pierre had worked out the whole scheme in his head. French Canada could become wealthy through her export of beaver pelts to Europe. First it would be necessary to build a few trading posts along this lonely shore. There the traders would live until spring brought Sioux and Crees from the south, loaded with bales of fur.

Pierre spent all summer exploring that completely unknown coast and voyaging among the islands near it. The Indians were overjoyed at his promise to return with ships to this region on the shore of the Bay of the North.

The Crees started back to Lake Superior when summer was nearly over. Pierre knew that it was too late in the year to try and get back to Three Rivers. He and Médard would have to spend another winter in the neighborhood of the Great Lakes. They went home with the Crees to the village where they had nearly starved to death. There they settled down to wait for signs of spring. This time they must have made sure there was plenty of food in the larder, or perhaps the winter was milder. At any rate, Pierre made no complaints about the way he and his partner lived until the spring.

As the days grew longer, a busy time arrived. Every Cree for miles around had beaver pelts which he wanted to exchange for French goods. Pierre arranged for an enormous fleet of canoes to meet on an appointed day and start off on the long voyage to Three Rivers. The Crees said they were not afraid of the Iroquois or anyone else. They would go with the Frenchmen to the towns on the St. Lawrence.

Eight hundred Crees turned up for the trip.

They came in great canoes and little canoes, new canoes and old, leaky ones. There were canoes that would carry three or four Indians besides a huge pile of pelts and others that would take only a man and his wife. But every canoe had its heavy load of pelts. Pierre knew that if only he could get the fleet down to Three Rivers, he would be doing a great service to his country. The money from the sale of all those pelts would enrich the little colony.

Four hundred and fifty canoes set out from the village. They swept along the lake, down past Sault Sainte Marie, and into the French River. The Indians had never thought of putting sails in their craft. They stared while Pierre rigged his canoe, and then hastened to follow his example. Steady winds carried the enormous fleet across the lakes at a speed greater than any Indian canoes had ever before attained.

Trouble began before the party reached the Ottawa River. They encountered a few Iroquois near Lake Nipissing and there was a short fight in which, however, no one was hurt. The Iroquois ran away into the forest.

"But," said the alarmed Crees, "they are the

scouts of a larger party. Their friends will wait to attack us farther down the river."

Pierre tried to encourage them. He assured them eight hundred well-armed Crees would be able to deal with any Iroquois war party they met. But the Crees were not persuaded. Some had their wives or daughters with them. They objected to fighting in a strange country. Finally they announced flatly that they would go home and try again next year.

Pierre was wild with rage and disappointment. He had spent two years planning this trip. Now, when it was half accomplished, it was about to be ruined by fear of a few miserable Iroquois. He argued with the Crees for days. He begged them to make a camp so that they could all listen to him.

"Do not go back," he said. "Think of the fine things you can buy at Quebec. Do you wish the Iroquois to laugh at you as cowards?"

The Crees began to take heart. Perhaps, they thought, there really were no more Iroquois waiting down the river. Perhaps the way actually was open for the acquisition of the fine steel swords and muskets they desired. It might be worth while taking a chance and making the trip after all. They agreed to go on.

Eight hundred Crees got back into their canoes. Down the Ottawa River they went, watching the banks fearfully for signs of an ambush. None was sighted. The voyage was peaceful from start to finish.

Cheering settlers at Montreal and Three Rivers stared in amazement as the huge fleet came into sight. There was great excitement at Quebec.

"In what country have you been?" asked surprised Frenchmen as they watched bale after bale of beaver skins piled upon the shore. "From whence do you come? We never saw the like of this. Those pelts will be prized like gold in France."

The angry Governor d'Argenson hastened to the spot. He had never forgotten how the two explorers had left Three Rivers without his permission. He was not interested in the wonderful cargo Pierre had brought or the discovery of a fur trail to Hudson Bay. All he cared about was revenge.

Pierre and Médard sold their own furs for a

hundred thousand dollars, and the money was
in their pockets when d'Argenson ordered them
both to appear before him. He fined them eighty
thousand dollars. With the remaining twenty
thousand they would have to buy trade goods
for their next expedition, as well as repay themselves for what they had spent during their two
years on the lakes. What this amounted to was
that after all their labors they were left almost
bankrupt.

In getting his revenge d'Argenson had ruined
two of the finest explorers ever known to French
Canada. He had also ruined France's hope of
building up a prosperous French colony in Canada. Never again would Pierre Radisson bring
back news of fresh discoveries. Never again
would he risk his life finding furs for Quebec.
What angered Pierre most was the fact that the
governor had put the greater part of the fine in
his own pocket.

"He did grease his chops with it," wrote
the furious Pierre, "in order that he might
grow rich by the labours of others and be
able to keep a coach and horses at Paris."

Pierre, the happy-go-lucky explorer, was finished. There was no one in French Canada to whom he could complain. Only one man had the power to give him back his money. That man was the king of France. Médard boarded a ship in Quebec and went to see him.

## Chapter Nine

*PIERRE AT THE
COURT OF KINGS*

D<small>AY</small> after day Médard hung round the huge, gilded rooms of the royal palace in Paris. He spoke to various important people who were friends of King Louis and told them why he was there. They all said that before long he would certainly have a chance to explain the reason for his trip. Their promises meant nothing. Louis was far more interested in going hunting, enjoying a feast, or dancing the quadrille at a ball than he was in listening to Médard.

Médard was not used to being kept waiting.

He disliked the powdered and painted courtiers
in their wigs and fine silks. At last he grew tired
of hanging about in that stuffy palace, which
smelled of perfumes and drains. He preferred
the pure fragrance of Canadian cedar forests.
He marched out of the palace and sailed straight
back to Quebec, where Pierre awaited him.

It was clear that Governor d'Argenson had
taken their money for good. There was no way
of getting it back from him.

"No one will help us, my friend," said Pierre,
"so we must help ourselves. Perhaps we may find
someone somewhere who will listen to our idea
about the Bay of the North. We are not to blame
if it is not a Frenchman."

There was an English governor at Nova Scotia.
Pierre went and saw him. The Englishman was
interested and promised the explorers a ship as
soon as possible. The vessel was not ready until
August but the two partners sailed in her then
for Hudson Bay. They figured that they could
spend the winter building a trading post and be
ready for the Crees when they came north next
spring.

The captain of the ship had never been in

cold seas until he set off on this voyage. When he saw the gleaming icebergs floating on the sea at the entrance to the bay, he became frightened. He refused to go any farther. Turning the ship about, he went back to Nova Scotia.

Pierre still would not give up. He could have scraped together enough money to buy a little farm on the St. Lawrence and settle down on it for the rest of his life, but he had seen the Bay of the North. He knew that his idea about shipping furs by way of it was a good one. Someone, he felt sure, must listen to him sooner or later. He went south to Boston and spoke to many rich merchants. Once again he was promised a ship. The vessel was on a voyage at the time. When she came back, Pierre was told, her captain would take him to Hudson Bay so that he might trade there for furs. The ship was wrecked at sea. The man who had promised her to Pierre was ruined. Nothing more could be done in Boston.

There was one more person who might be interested. King Charles the Second of England liked ships and explorers. He was always ready to listen to men with ideas and even more ready to talk about ways of making money.

Pierre and Médard sailed for England in an English ship. Four days out from land a Dutch warship came in sight. She opened fire with her guns and smashed up the masts and hull of the English vessel. Her crew then boarded the English ship and captured the crew after a fight. Being French, the explorers took no part in the skirmish. It was not their concern that England and Holland were at war with each other. It must have been one of the very few times when the two men stood back and let others do the fighting.

Ever since Pierre had seen the Bay of the North, he had met with nothing but misfortune. The Dutch ship landed him in Holland. From there he had to make his way to England. He reached London only to find that a frightful pestilence was killing off hundreds of citizens daily. King Charles had fled with his court to the town of Oxford. The partners hired a couple of horses and rode there. While they waited to see the king, they learned to speak and write an extraordinary kind of English. Médard never got much farther than learning to call for more beer, but Pierre became quite fluent.

The time came at last when they were standing in front of the English king, telling the fascinated monarch about their wild fights and journeys. King Charles was interested in Hudson
Bay. He promised Pierre a ship. It seemed now
that finally everything was going to be all right.
The explorers hoped that before long they
would be buying furs from their friends, the
Crees.

The ship they were to take was lying alongside
a wooden wharf in the Thames River. Before
they could go aboard her, the great fire of London started. The city blazed for over a week.
Roaring flames set fire to the wharf and the ship
was destroyed. Vessels were hard to come by at
that time, and Charles was unable to let Pierre
have another. He promised, however, that in a
year or so he might be able to provide another
ship.

Pierre waited for two years, but then he was
given two ships, the *Eaglet* and the *Nonsuch*.
They were dreadful little tubs.

Pierre looked at them in disgust. "One of us
will go in each," he said to Médard. "If the one
is drowned, the other may live. He who lives will

be able to guide others to Hudson Bay. But if we both drown, who will speak with the Crees and the Sioux?"

A storm hit both vessels before they were half-way across the Atlantic. Pierre's ship, the *Eaglet*, was badly damaged. She had to stagger back to England. The *Nonsuch*, with Médard aboard, was last seen plunging westward into the storm.

Pierre went to London and stayed there, wondering if Médard had been drowned. There was no way of finding out; he could only wait and see if his partner ever turned up again.

The *Nonsuch* actually reached Hudson Bay. She sailed up it in the early fall, with floating ice bumping her rotten sides. In James Bay, at the southern end of Hudson Bay, she dropped anchor. The noise of that chain rattling down must have been a welcome sound to Médard. At last he was back in the Bay of the North.

He hurried ashore. With planks and iron spikes, with pitch and nails, he and a couple of sailors built the first trading post that ever stood on Hudson Bay. It was christened Fort Rupert after a relation of King Charles, and the river on which it stood was named the Rupert River.

Thanks to Governor d'Argenson, an English trading post was built on that lonely shore instead of a French one.

While Pierre fretted in London, worrying about his old partner, Médard was busily trading with the Indians who came north in the spring. They were overjoyed to see him again after so long. Had they known he was coming, they said, they would have brought many more furs. They were able to scrape together just enough to fill the *Nonsuch*. In return they were given more muskets, knives, and cooking pots than they had ever dreamed of. They went home delighted, promising to come back next spring.

The *Nonsuch* was back in England by August. Pierre and Médard hugged each other for sheer joy. Together they rushed down to where the ship was lying and looked at the furs.

The pelts were of finer quality than any the English had ever seen. Rich merchants impatiently lined up to buy them. They handed over eighty thousand dollars for the lot. Even after allowing for the cost of the voyage, there was a profit of seventy thousand dollars for the partners.

Everyone who had sneered at the explorers suddenly wanted to become friends with them. Everyone wanted to put up money for another voyage in return for a share of the profits. Everyone wanted to ask Pierre and Médard out to dinner. Suddenly they were the most popular men in London. Wherever they went they were asked to describe their fights and voyages across Canada.

The partners knew how little such popularity was worth. Pierre was sick of Europe. He longed for the smell of the forest and the sound of swift-flowing rivers. America was calling him back across the Atlantic. He was impatient to go.

A number of rich gentlemen put up the money for the voyage. King Charles gave them the right to keep Hudson Bay for themselves. From now on no one else could go there; no one else could even buy a beaver pelt there. King Charles forgot only one thing: Canada belonged to France and not to England. He had no right to give Hudson Bay to Pierre or to give anyone permission even to go there.

The bay had put a curse on Pierre. Even now, when things were going better with him, ill luck interfered. The greedy Englishmen were so busy counting the profits they were going to make that they quite forgot who had given them the idea about Hudson Bay. None of them even tried to be polite to the explorers. They finally offered Pierre and Médard a tiny share in the profits but only at the last moment did they think of doing so.

Pierre agreed to accept this small reward. By then he was so eager to get back to Canada that he would have agreed to anything. In the spring of 1671 three ships left England for Hudson Bay. The explorers were on board one of them.

Pierre was delighted to be back in the land he loved so much. Six years had passed since he had last been in Canada. He scrambled ashore as fast as he could.

The Crees standing on the beach surrounded him with excited greetings. "We believed you would never come back to us," they said. "Why have you been so long away?"

"Because I had to find ships for your furs," Pierre explained. "Such matters take time. But from now on I will remain with you as I did in the old days."

Pierre built another trading post on the western shore of James Bay. There he and Médard settled down to trade with the Indians. Once again they were together. They were happy in their work and were liked by the Indians. The Bay of the North was no longer a dream.

But they forgot that this time they were not trading on their own account. The Englishmen back in London were running things.

Word passed among the tribes that white men were living near the bay and buying all the furs they could get. French priests heard the story and before long it reached Quebec.

Governor d'Argenson had gone back to Paris. Another governor had taken his place who sadly realized what his country had lost through her shabby treatment of the explorers. He wrote to King Louis of France, asking him to try and get Pierre back into the service of France.

Meanwhile the three English ships sailed back home, their holds stuffed with pelts. Pierre went, too. In London he had met and fallen in love with a beautiful girl named Mary Kirke. He was going back to marry her.

A few days after the wedding Pierre went to

see the English merchants. He was as rudely
treated as ever. The sum of money he was offered
as his share of the profits was four hundred dollars. The furs he had brought from the bay had
sold at a profit of one hundred and fifty thousand. This kind of treatment was too much even
for easygoing Pierre. He was still angry about it
when he received a letter from Paris. King Louis
wanted to see him.

Pierre went to France, tired of trying to make
a living for himself by dealing with the miserly
London merchants.

Louis welcomed him like an old friend. "The
English have treated you badly, my Pierre," he
said. "Serve France and you will be better re-
warded. A ship is ready for you. Go in her to
your Hudson Bay and bring back as many furs
as you can."

Pierre asked for time to think about the matter. He loved his wife, whose strict parents, he
knew, would never allow her to leave England.
If he were going to work for France, there would
not be many chances of visiting London. But of
what use was it to be with his wife without
money enough to live on? Pierre made up his

mind to accept King Louis' offer. Three weeks later he was sailing across the Atlantic.

The Quebec governor had two ships ready for him. While they were being loaded, Pierre waited for Médard. He knew that his partner, arrived now in England, would have read the letter Pierre had left for him. Médard had never had a great liking for the English. The miserable way they had treated him now made him like them even less. As Pierre had expected, Médard turned up in Quebec, happy to work for France.

The partners sailed north in July 1683. It had taken them eighteen years to find a French ship ready to make the voyage. What a waste of time it had been! They were no longer young men. They had wasted the best years of their lives trying to show the wisdom of using the Bay of the North. It had been a long time to spend trying to make something out of an idea. They had succeeded at last, but the secret was no longer a secret. Jealous ears had listened when the explorers had spoken of their discovery. Other men had become eager to share the riches of the Bay of the North.

*Chapter Ten*

## PIERRE RADISSON'S
## LAST ADVENTURES

THE awful loneliness and drifting icebergs frightened the crews of the French ships. Time after time they swore they would go no farther. Pierre calmed them down. He had had plenty of experience in dealing with apprehensive men. White sailors afraid of icebergs were not much different from Indians afraid of the Iroquois on the Ottawa River. The ships sailed on until they reached Hudson Bay.

Beside the mouth of a wide river Pierre built

another trading post. Above it flew the flag of France. The partners and a few ships' officers set off along the coast in a canoe, hoping to find Indians. They came across a party camped on the shore. None of them knew Pierre, for they were mostly young warriors. But when Pierre spoke to them in their own language, they invited him to sit down and eat with them.

At the end of the meal an Indian pulled a homemade knife out of his purse and tried to hack a piece off the lump of tobacco Pierre had given him. The blade, made of soft iron, bent in the Indian's hand.

Pierre calmly took the useless knife and dropped it in the fire. "It makes me sad to see my friends using such things," he said. "Sell me your furs and I will give you knives of good steel."

One of the Indians stared at Pierre. "There has been only one white man who ever treated us like that," he said. "Others would be afraid. You must be the man of whom our fathers speak, he who came and stayed in our villages for two winters."

"I am he," said Pierre.

"Good!" said the Indian. "Our fathers loved you and so will we. You shall have all our furs. To none other will we sell them."

Pierre sent the Indians to the trading post he had built. He and his companions continued their trip. Next day there came an unpleasant surprise. On rounding a bend, Pierre sighted a ship anchored close to the shore. On the beach were white men and they seemed to be building some kind of a house.

Pierre crept forward that night and got near the ship without being seen. He could hear the men speaking together. The language was English. Those London merchants, he thought, had been unwilling to give up sending ships to the bay merely because Pierre and his partner had left England. This must be a new party they had organized.

Next morning Pierre got into a canoe by himself. He went to the anchored ship and called to some of the crew. "Whence do you come?"

A big young fellow looked over the side. "We are from Boston," he called back. "I am captain and my name is Ben Gillam."

Boston! This was bad news for Pierre. Some

New England merchants must have stolen his
own idea.

"Who gave you permission to come here?"
asked Pierre. "This bay belongs to France."

"I have no permission," Gillam said carelessly, "but who is there to stop me?"

Who was there indeed? The New England
ship was a sturdy little vessel, heavily armed with
guns, any one of which could have sunk Pierre's
worm-eaten craft in a couple of minutes. There
was no point in making an enemy. Pierre went
aboard Ben Gillam's ship and made friends with
him. But all the time they were laughing and
chatting together, Pierre's brain was busy. This
bay belonged to France. No one else was going
to take pelts from here. He was still wondering
what to do when he got back into his canoe and
returned to the spot where his friends were waiting for him.

The Frenchmen were sitting round their fire
that night when they heard sounds coming across
the dark waters of the bay. Canvas was flapping
and banging against wooden masts and spars.
An anchor chain rattled down. Another ship
had arrived.

In the morning Pierre looked seaward through the mist. A fine big vessel was lying half a mile away. As he watched, a boat was lowered over her side. Men jumped into it and began rowing towards the shore. Pierre sent his friends in among the trees and waited alone for the boat to draw nearer.

The craft was thirty yards from shore when Pierre swung up his heavy musket. "Halt!" he shouted. "Come nearer and I fire."

A fat, red-faced man in the stern of the boat rose to his feet. He was dressed in clothes of fine quality and seemed a most important person.

He glared at the apparent Indian in ragged deerskins. "What the devil do you mean?" he roared. "By what right do you stop us in this manner? Put that gun down at once. Put it down, my good man."

"This bay belongs to France," said Pierre. "I have claimed it for my country." He raised his musket.

The alarmed men in the boat saw half a dozen figures, with Médard at their head, step from among the trees. Each man had a musket and they were all pointing at the boat.

The Englishman sat down with a sudden jerk. "Sir," he said in a milder voice, "I have been sent out as governor of Hudson Bay. I understood the bay belonged to England. I came in a ship captained by Zechariah Gillam. My name is Bridgar, Governor Bridgar."

Pierre grinned. He had met old Zechariah Gillam and disliked him heartily. But this was really funny. Zechariah Gillam was captain of an English vessel that had brought a governor to claim Hudson Bay. Lower down the bay, Ben Gillam, old Zechariah's son, was trying to get furs for New England without the permission of either England or France. Men from three different regions had all arrived within a day or so of one another. Sooner or later there would certainly be trouble.

Pierre once more decided to be polite and plan later what to do. The governor of Quebec had told him to claim Hudson Bay for France. Louis had ordered him to do the same thing. He was only carrying out his orders in stopping Governor Bridgar from claiming it for England.

"Since you are here by an unfortunate mistake, sir," said Pierre, "there is no harm in your

remaining on French soil as a guest. The year
grows late. Remain here until the spring if you
wish."

Bridgar's humor became better. He was not
sure what to do. Claiming a bay for one's country
was quite all right so long as no one pointed
muskets at you and forbade you to claim it. He
asked Pierre to dinner aboard the ship.

Pierre told tall stories in the cabin that evening. He said that four or five French forts were
already being built along the shores of the bay.
There were a dozen men in each. Three French
ships were anchored farther down James Bay.
Another ship was expected to arrive before winter. Governor Bridgar believed all this stuff. He
never suspected that Pierre had only two small
ships moored in a river manned by only twenty-
five sailors. Nor did he know that not a single
French fort had been built. He was thankful
that he had not tried to be difficult with this
Frenchman.

For the next three days Pierre and Médard remained hidden in the woods while they continued to watch the English vessel. They wanted to
know what Bridgar would do. Apparently there

was only one thing the governor wanted—a warm house in which to spend the long, icy winter. The crew of his ship began building a snug little cottage on the shore. The sight made Pierre feel better. He went back to his trading post and started trading for furs with the Indians as fast as he could.

A week or so afterwards he went back to see how the Americans and English were getting along. Young Ben Gillam had built himself a strong little fort, armed with guns taken out of his ship. He was not nearly so friendly when he saw Pierre coming. The Crees had told Ben they were going to trade with the man who had been their fathers' friend. Nothing the young New Englander said could make them change their minds.

Pierre next visited Governor Bridgar, who was living in his hut now. His ship still lay anchored offshore.

"Take care of your ship when the ice comes, my friend," Pierre said to old Zechariah Gillam, "or the ice will close round her and smash her sides."

"I want no advice as to how to manage my

own ship," grumbled the old skipper. "I can look after her well enough myself."

Pierre shrugged his shoulders and went away. He went back to his post and continued to buy furs.

Governor Bridgar began to grow a little suspicious of Pierre towards the end of the summer. He had not seen any other French ships sailing down the bay nor any other Frenchmen. He wondered if Pierre had been fooling him. He sent a party southward to search for the forts that were supposed to guard the coast. The English sailors, after rowing several miles, sighted Ben Gillam's fort in the distance. They returned in haste to their ship and told the governor that Pierre had spoken the truth. There was a very fine French fort only a short distance away!

Bridgar became angry. He had looked forward to being the first governor of Hudson Bay. Now that the French were so well established, he had no chance at all. He began to dislike Pierre.

Ben Gillam's men had seen the distant ship. The New Englander was impatiently awaiting Pierre's next visit in order to tell him about it.

"It is true," said Pierre. "The English have arrived, but do not be afraid, my friend. I have told them this bay belongs to France. They have no more right here than you have."

"My fort gives me my right," Ben said angrily. "Neither you nor anyone else can put me out of it."

The remark was a stupid one to make to an old Indian fighter. Then and there Pierre decided the time had come to take Ben's fort away from him.

But first he paddled through the thickening ice to call on Governor Bridgar. He found him in a very bad temper. Old Zechariah Gillam was in a much worse one. He had not followed Pierre's advice, and the ice had closed in round the ship and smashed its oaken sides. The English had lost their fine vessel. Even worse, they had lost most of their rations with it. It looked as if Governor Bridgar and his unhappy crew were going to spend a cold and hungry winter.

Pierre saw his chance. He was the only person who could supply the English with food. They were no longer in a position to argue with him about anything. He had them where he wanted them. He went back to his trading post and sent a canoe piled high with food. The journey was a difficult one. Hudson Bay was beginning to freeze over for the winter. Only a narrow channel, filling with chunks of ice, remained open. Future journeys would have to be made across the frozen surface of the bay.

Pierre visited Ben Gillam again. The young man was becoming very difficult.

"I do not believe your stories," he said. "I doubt whether France has a single fort in the whole of Hudson Bay. If there are any, show me one."

"Come with me to our trading post," Pierre replied. "There you will see my ships and meet many other Frenchmen. There, too, will you see my official papers from the governor of Quebec."

Ben Gillam walked right into the trap. "I will come," he said.

At the end of an excellent meal at the trading post, Pierre broke the news to Ben. "Now that you are here," he said, "I fear you cannot leave again. I intend to seize your ship and your fort in the name of France."

Ben flew into a rage. He called Pierre every name he could think of. He thumped the table with his fist and swore that no Frenchman was going to make a prisoner of him. "As for my fort," he sneered, "you will never get near it. My men will blow you to pieces first."

Pierre smiled. "I will have your fort—and your ship—inside of a week," he said quietly.

At this Ben lost control of himself. He had to be taken away, bellowing with rage, and locked up in a room whose low temperature would soon cool him down.

Pierre and eight men marched across the ice, pulling a sled. The New England fort stood black and solid against the white of snow and ice. The Frenchmen approached it carelessly, their muskets slung across their backs. They were laughing and talking cheerfully among themselves. No one could have imagined a less warlike party.

The officer whom Ben had left in charge never dreamed anything might be wrong. He recognized Pierre and Médard. He drew back the heavy bolts and opened the door. "Where is Captain Gillam?" he asked.

"Coming," said Pierre. "He was delayed for a short time."

The officer and three of his men closed the door. For a few seconds their backs were turned. They swung around when they had finished and suddenly stopped. Each found himself looking into the black muzzle of a heavy pistol.

Médard and the remaining Frenchmen entered the room where the rest of the garrison were chatting or playing cards. The men looked up and blinked with surprise. They, too, were confronted by pistols. Pierre had taken Ben Gillam's fort.

The garrison were locked up in a room after being disarmed. Two men were left to guard them. Pierre, Médard, and five others walked out to the New England ship lying on the ice. They climbed aboard without interference and took the ship as they had taken the fort.

"I regret to say you are all my prisoners," Pierre announced.

A member of the crew laughed. "That's fair enough," he said. "I reckon we'll be no worse off than we were with Ben Gillam. He's treated us like curs since we sailed out of Boston."

Pierre felt better. He had been wondering how he and his few companions could guard so many English prisoners. He no longer had to worry. The crew were quite ready to do as they were told. None of them was in the least anxious to help their captain. On the contrary, they cheered when Pierre told them he had been locked up.

The Frenchmen collected all the muskets and pistols from the fort and the ship and loaded them on their sled. The crew would be helpless without arms, even if they came to dislike being prisoners. But that seemed unlikely. The sailors were clearly anxious to go on living peacefully in their comfortable, warm ship until spring put an end to the accursed cold of Hudson Bay in wintertime.

Only Governor Bridgar and his men were still to be dealt with. They were in a poor position to give trouble, but Pierre wanted to make sure. He decided it would be a good idea to visit the English and take over all the weapons they had managed to save before their ship sank. If they refused to hand them over, they would receive no more sled loads of food.

Governor Bridgar was unhappy. He loathed the freezing gales howling across the bay, the everlasting cold, and the driving sleet. Stranded in this desolate region of encircling ice, alone except for his crew living in hastily built huts, he was past caring about anything but his store of brandy. He gave orders to hand over all fire-arms, cursed Pierre for a sly Frenchman, and went back to the brandy.

Pierre was in complete command of Hudson Bay.

The days began to lengthen. Spring was coming and the frozen bay groaned as its load of ice started to melt. Patches of green water appeared in April and Pierre made ready to leave. The storeroom of his house was packed with beautiful pelts. He wanted to unload them in Quebec and return promptly to meet the Indians when they came north.

The French ships were almost falling apart. They were wholly unfit to make another long voyage. Governor Bridgar's once fine vessel was a mass of splintered timber and spars. Only one good sound ship remained, Ben Gillam's. Pierre took her and loaded her up with his furs, the

English crews, his Frenchmen, Governor Bridgar, and the angry Ben Gillam. Old Zechariah Gillam was so startled by the sudden appearance of Ben that he gave no trouble to anyone. His son was locked up but he remained free.

The crowded ship reached the St. Lawrence. Pierre knew he had done his duty to France. He had claimed Hudson Bay for his country, arrested the trespassers, and brought back a magnificent load of furs. During the coming summer more French posts could be built round the shores of the bay. When next winter came, no ships belonging to other nations would dare enter. In a cheerful mood Pierre went to see the governor.

A cruel and stupid France broke the gallant old explorer's heart. A new governor was ruling in Quebec. He rebuked Pierre for making prisoners of the English and the men from Boston. He reported the matter to France and released Governor Bridgar, the Gillams, and their crews. Englishmen and New Englanders sailed away to freedom.

A reply came from the royal court in Paris. It said that France wanted no quarrel with England for the time being. If the English wished to have Hudson Bay, let them have it. French Canada would have to get along without it. Meanwhile, Pierre Radisson and Médard Groseilliers must be punished for having dared to imprison the trespassers. Their share of the profits on the fur cargo would be seized. It amounted to fifty thousand dollars. Neither of them ever received one single cent.

The Quebec governor had only recently arrived from France. He knew nothing about the lives of the two fine men he had been ordered to punish and no doubt cared less. The wealth belonging to the explorers was carelessly poured into the bottomless money chests of France.

Pierre and Médard were ruined. After all their gallant adventures and high courage an ungrateful country had robbed them of their reward. That was the end for two tired and heartbroken men.

Médard went back to his little farm on the St. Lawrence River. He was an old man now but he lived for several years and died peacefully.

Pierre tried once more to mend his fortunes. He went to Paris and sought in vain to get King

Louis to restore the money seized from him. He was treated in a rude, careless manner. Now that Hudson Bay had been taken over by the English, no one wanted to listen to the man who had dreamed of making it a great fur center. Utterly disgusted and angry, Pierre left France forever.

What could he do now? He was too old to start trading again with the Indians as he had done in his youth. The fur was going up north to the bay. The Indians who carried it were no longer the men who had known Pierre in his days of greatness.

Pierre went back to England. As soon as he got there, France declared him a traitor. He had gone to live with the English. From now on he was no subject of France. Pierre became a man without a nation. A reward for his capture was offered by the French government. Had he gone back to Canada, he would have been arrested at once.

England was the only place where Pierre could stay. He had to remain there. For a few years he helped the Hudson's Bay Company to strengthen its grip on the fur trade. In return he met with nothing except suspicion and ingratitude. He was paid a tiny salary and fell into debt. Mary, the beautiful wife he had hardly known, died. He spent the last few years of his life in London, a friendless old man without even enough money to pay the rent of a comfortable room. He died at the age of seventy-four, somewhere about the year 1711. His quest had brought him nothing save unhappiness.

It may be that in those last few years the sight of the River Thames, when evening fell and dark shadows hid the grubby houses on the far side, reminded Pierre of another and mightier river flowing through cedar forests on its way to the ocean. Once again he may have recalled the glory of the lakes at sunrise and their peace under the stars. Perhaps there even stirred in him an echo of the triumph that had filled him when first he beheld the Bay of the North.

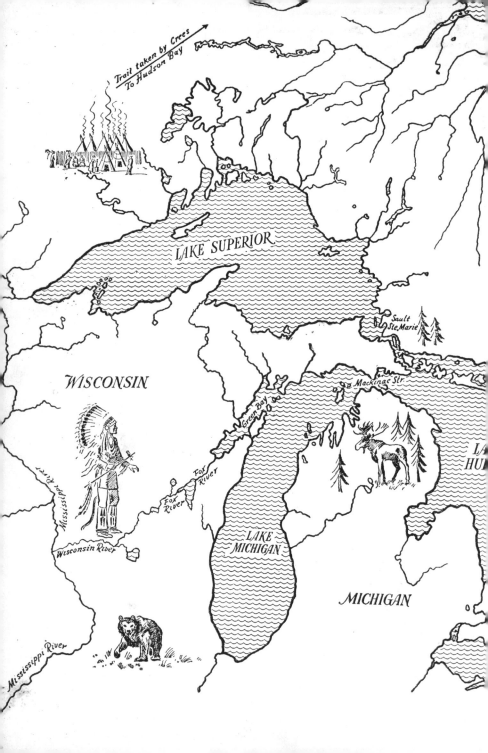

Trail taken by Crees
To Hudson Bay

LAKE SUPERIOR

Sault
Ste. Marie

WISCONSIN

Mackinac Str.

Green Bay

Fox River

Fox River

LA
HU

Mississippi River

LAKE MICHIGAN

Wisconsin River

MICHIGAN

Mississippi River